Ayur Cooking

Shanti Gowans

JAICO PUBLISHING HOUSE

Mumbai Delhi Bangalore Kolkata
Hyderabad Chennai Ahmedabad Bhopal

Published by Jaico Publishing House
121 Mahatma Gandhi Road
Mumbai - 400 001
jaicopub@vsnl.com
www.jaicobooks.com

© Shanti Gowans

AYURVEDIC COOKING
ISBN 81-7992-055-0

First Jaico Impression: 2004
Fifth Jaico Impression: 2007

Printed by
Snehesh Printers
320-A, Shah & Nahar Ind. Est. A-1
Lower Parel, Mumbai - 400 013.

Acknowledgements

This has truly been a group project. Where do I begin to thank the many students, teachers, authors - many of whom I have not met and many whose names I do not even know, who have made this knowledge and these perennial philosophies possible?

With deep love and gratitude I thank Christine Gleeson for her encouragement and sometimes insistence about this book and Sonja Stauder for her commitment to my work. Both have road tested the recipes, prepared and presented them, feeding others at the Centre, and on occassion even taught them at cooking classes - all in the spirit of dedication to their beliefs and tastebuds.

My gratitude and thanks to Alka Tyle and her mum, Usha Agarwal for proof-correcting the Indian words, and supplying the blanks, wherever.

To the many students who attended 'Kitchen Pharmacy & The Yoga of Food', and cheerfully volunteered to be my 'guinea pigs', I offer choicest blessings that you may transform your dreams into reality and touch the lives of many people throughout the world.

Most importantly, we thank the Divine Power that brings Yoga into our lives.

Recipes	Shanti Gowans
	Christine Gleeson
	Sonja Stauder
Editing	Sonja Stauder. Carmel Hogan.

CONTENTS

From This arose   Space;
from Space,   Wind;
from Wind,   Fire;
from Fire,   Water;
from Water,   Earth;
from Earth,   Plants;
from Plants,   Nutriment;
from Nutriment,   Man.

Taittiriya Upanishad.

Part One: Healthy Mind, Healthy Body

1. HEALTHY MIND, HEALTHY BODY
MENS SANA IN CORPORE SANO

Good health
is
having no fatigue,
having a good appetite,
going to sleep and waking easily,
having a good memory,
good humour,
precision in thought and action,
being honest, humble, grateful and loving.

We don't eat the same food... But we all eat.

Why we eat produces one answer ... to satisfy hunger. But when asked *what* you eat, each person gives a different response. Some say "I love Italian food," others might say "I follow a macrobiotic diet," still others might say "I like plain food" and so on.

Eat any food you want. Call it by any name you want. Choose your own way to satisfy your own taste, temperament and capacity. There is no need to criticise or condemn those who follow a different path. ... Spiritual hunger is the same in all, the 'food' to satisfy that hunger may vary.

Your spiritual health lies in your ability to live in harmony with the external universe. Your mental health is dependent upon your ability to live in harmony with yourself.

Your mental condition has both a physical and social impact.

You are the guardian and custodian of this planet. Your own survival depends upon not disturbing the fragile balance between nature and living organisms. You must prevent wanton destruction and return to the equilibrium of nature. If you cut down a tree for your own use, plant another. Ensure the purity of water by not polluting the waterways and ocean, directly or indirectly. Ensure that the air is not poisoned.

To enjoy spiritual rewards and to be fit and healthy, you need to eat properly. Your body and mind need the best food to give you your nutrients. The food you consume becomes your appearance, your mode of expression and has a vital influence on your state of happiness.

There are many factors which affect the foods we choose. Various agendas, ranging from moods, the ease with which we can obtain our food, cultural background, time, ignorance or disbelief in the concept of chemical overload, prejudice … tempt us to place convenience before quality. The dangers of becoming addicted to the immediately satiating effects of fast food are well known. Refined sugars, flours, starches and chemical additives begin their trail of damage by stimulating false appetites resulting in us being overfed and undernourished. Your body will only accept so much abuse before registering strong disapproval. Listen and understand your body's messages. Recognise the damage unnatural substances wreak. Every human disease, ranging from cardiovascular problems, cancers, degenerative disorders etc. have been linked in one way or another to diet. Malfunctioning of the digestive process is the first symptom of all disease.

You must recognise the importance of nourishing your body with life-giving foods. A balanced diet of natural foods is the best way to energise and revitalise. We are entering an era where people are taking a more spiritual and respectful approach to their bodies. Be more aware ... more in tune with your body's inner voice. Your goal is to develop your own individual immune system to such a degree that the body become's its own best physician. Let your food be your medicine. Most people who have been exposed to Ayurvedic vegetarian cooking do not just accept it but are happily converted to the healthy style of eating it offers. Your only regret will be that you didn't discover it a lot earlier.

2. THE YOGA OF FOOD

Deha Vijnana is the Yogic science pertaining to a deeper understanding of the human body and the subtle forces that regulate its functions. This science deals not only with the physical structure of the body, such as muscular, skeletal and neurological systems but also with *Svara Vijnana*, the science of breath, of *pranic* (life) force and its intricate pathways, the *nadi* system.

All that exists in the macrocosm exists in the microcosm - *Surya Vijnana*, the mystical sciences of the sun; pertaining to exploring the source of life and *Chandra Vidya*, the Lunar science; the science of the mystical moon, also known as *Soma Vidya*. The natural balance of life is represented by solar and lunar functions which connect mind and body through balancing life force extracted from nature, including one's own nature.

'*Annam Brahman* - Food is God ... Food is consciousness', proclaim the ancient Vedic texts. All the great wisdom traditions of the world have looked upon the miracle of nutrition as something sacred. Food is an expression of the same universal mind that creates your body and has the same level of manifestation that comprises your physical form. The same spirit or universal energy that animates everything that lives, moves and breathes, exists in food.

More than mere calories, fibre, carbohydrates, proteins, fats, minerals, vitamins and water; food is intelligence ... and love. You too are intelligence and in constant and dynamic exchange with universal intelligence through physiological processes, of which eating is the most important. Eating, digestion and metabolism transform one mode of intelligence into another.

You began as a speck of information on a DNA molecule, food was added ... the same food was transformed into your brain, intellect and ego. The life energy in a grain of rice today may become a light receptor in your eye tomorrow, decoding the intelligence of the universe into colour and form. Give thanks, enjoy, celebrate and cherish both the preparation and satisfaction from each meal.

Yoga *per se*, does not say much about diet and not all Yogic authorities, ancient or modern, are in agreement over what constitutes a good diet. However without exception, they emphasise the importance of exercising restraint over the intake of food. This principle is known as *mitahara*, which means moderate diet. *Mita* means proportionate, or enough to nourish. *Ahar* means food. *Mitahari*, has therefore come to mean *moderation in eating*, or balance in food.

For there to be a tranquility in everything, do not go to extremes. Place a limit on things and pursue the middle path. Yoga is not for the person who eats too much or fasts extensively. Just as you like to think in a Yogic way, also eat in a Yogic way. When you let all your actions, words and thoughts be Yogic, your life is completely transformed.

A normal diet gives us the physical energy and all that is necessary for the body, but as we agree, the benefit of the diet does not stop here.

3. SATTWAS, RAJAS, TAMAS

The Hindu texts speak of three qualities, *gunas*, present in all life, including food. *Sattwa* is the tranquil state, *Rajas* the very active state and *Tamas* the state of inertia or dullness.

- *Sattwic* food is variously understood as contributing to serenity, providing the essentials, keeping the human organism sweet and clean. It is pure food.
- *Rajistic* food contributes to dynamism, making one active.
- *Tamasic* food is sloth producing.
  Too much *Sattwic* or *Rajistic* food can be *Tamasic*.

The *Chandogya Upanishad* (VII.26.2) from the 8th century B.C. speaks of the close link between "dietary purity and purity of being."

The *Bhagavad Gita*, a pre-Christian work on non-dualistic Yoga, distinguishes foods according to the predominance of *Sattwa* (which embodies that which is pure and fine eg. sunlight), *Rajas* (which embodies the active principle eg. an erupting volcano) and *Tamas* (which embodies solidity and resistance eg. a block of granite) in them. Our mood and character vary according to the predominating *guna*, quality. The spiritual aspirant must overcome tamas by rajas and rajas by sattva… and then even transcend sattva.

'Foods that promote life, lucidity, strength, health, happiness and satisfaction and are savoury, rich in oil, firm and heartening are agreeable to those who are *Sattwa*-natured.

Foods that are pungent, sour, salty, spicy, sharp, harsh and burning are coveted by those who are Rajas-natured. They cause pain, grief and disease.

And (food) that is spoiled, tasteless, putrid, stale, left over and unclean, is food agreeable to those who are Tamas-natured (person).'

Bhagavad Gita (XVII. 8f).

Foods that are natural, not very spicy, sour or hot are considered to be Sattwic. This includes fruits, nuts, milk and milk products, steamed vegetables, cooked grains, beans and cereals. When the same Sattwic products are mixed with a lot of spices and become sour and hot, they become Rajastic. This means they create a restlessness in the mind. Rajastic food also includes meat and fish.

Hatha-Yoga-Pradipika (1:58) authored by Svatmarama who lived in the mid-fourteenth century AD. defines a Yogic diet as agreeable and nutritious food that is consumed in order to delight Lord Shiva. This work echoes widespread dietary wisdom when it stipulates that one should leave one fourth of the stomach empty. Overeating, *atyahara*, according to Hatha Yoga Pradipika (1.15) is one of the six factors by which Yoga is foiled.

Gheranada-Samhita (V.16ff.) states: "They who practise Yoga without moderation in diet incur various diseases and obtain no success."

Observe moderation in your diet, *mitahara*. Do not overload your stomach. Eat simple food like rice, bread, lentils, legumes, vegetables and fruits. Avoid depleted food without any life force.

Ahara Shuddhi is the purification of food. According to the scriptures, not only the body but also our thinking process is greatly affected by the food we eat. Over-fed and undernourished, our degenerative diseases arise from malnutrition, incomplete digestion and internal pollution, which can be reversed by nutrient enrichment, improved digestion and detoxification. The food you eat influences all of the following: your cardiovascular, immune and digestive systems; muscular and joint mobility; skin, hair and nails; bowel regularity; brain function, energy production, blood glucose stability, toxicity, overall health and wellbeing. The food you eat needs to be eaten in appropriate amounts, at the right time and with the right mental attitude. Without observing a dietary discipline, one cannot work successfully with oneself.

Become more 'food-aware.' Merely quantifying food in terms of calories and biochemical constituents is clinical, sterile and devoid of the mystery of life that is present in every act of eating. Modern nutritional science may tell us that the so-called nutrients imprisoned for extended periods of time, for instance in canned food (fortified with Vitamins etc.) contains all the nutrients we need chemically, however, in terms of Yogic life, there is less life-energy, *prana*, in processed foods.

Food is not a dead substance that exists just to 'fill a hole.' Food too has a soul. It is an alchemical process of transformation; a celebration of life. It provides you with sustenance and nourishment along your path of spiritual growth. Let your food be your medicine.

Make a commitment to transform and improve your life. Let this be reflected in your food choices. Develop a reverence for food and the miracle of transformation inherent in it. Bless all that you eat and drink with love, gratitude and Divine presence, so that it becomes wholesome and nutritious.

Live naturally and you will know what to eat and when. Do not get out of touch with yourself. Taste the flavour of love in your food. Let every meal you ingest be a conscious participation in the cosmic dance of transformation.

14

4. NATURAL HEALTH

The fundamental principle of true healing consists of a return to natural habits of living. We can apply this principle to food. The world needs a good diet - even if only to avoid the worries of enormous hospital bills. Even the most learned scientists who ever lived on this earth could not separate natural foods and then combine them in a better manner than nature herself has prepared them. Coming back to God's original plan for maintaining health, restoring the sick, using tried, safe and inexpensive remedies for the prevention of disease and sickness are what this book 'First Steps to Ayurvedic Vegetarian Cooking' is all about. It informs, educates and nudges you in the appropriate places and in a practical and enjoyable way so that you may learn to feast on the food prepared from the recipes provided.

The Creation stories tell us that human beings on this planet were fashioned out of the ground. The different properties which are found on this planet are found in human beings; the fruits, nuts, grains and vegetables contain the same elements which are in the earth and in human beings. When these fruits, nuts, grains and vegetables are eaten in their natural state and not perverted and robbed of their life giving properties by their preparation, health, beauty and happiness will be the sure reward.

No matter how many germs get into the body, if the blood stream is clean and the blood corpuscles are in a healthy condition, you will be safe. Everyone comes into contact with many kinds of germs, but these organisms will not harm you or cause you sickness and death, unless they have a place in which to propagate themselves.

In India, half a century ago , doctors were scarce. People

largely depended upon each other and their simple treatments of which they had empirical and practical knowledge. Basically it was very simple - when a physical law was obeyed, by any human being, whether good or bad they would reap the reward God had promised. For food we depended on nuts from the forests, fruits from the orchards, grains from the fields and water from rivers, streams and the well. For medicine and preventative medicine we used herbs from the fields and gardens, teas made from the inner bark of certain trees and shrubs and the health-giving, cooling juices of wild and harvested fruits that grew all around us in abundance. Herbs, we gathered and dried in the summertime, both for ourselves and our neighbours. We knew not to eat the foods that made us sick and to eat food in its natural and fresh state as far as possible. As a child I had no candy, ice cream, cakes or cookies of any description, nor any white flour, or cane sugar products.

Expand the statement 'you are what you eat' to include all of your senses. The mind 'digests' and interprets everything you take in. Everything you experience becomes a part of you just as your food does. The interactive roles that include your diet and nutrition, prevention of disease, fitness, lifestyle, attitude, time perception, exercise and rest, all need to be areas you focus your best intentions on for sustainable health.

A balanced diet is simply adequate nutrition, based on a wide variety of foods, providing energy, nutrients, dietary fibre and fluids in amounts appropriate for good health.

Ideally we would all be living in the mountains, breathing fresh air and getting plenty of sunshine. Our days would be spent outside with lots of exercise and meditation. In reality many of us live in a city, often with less than ideal environmental conditions.

A Yogic approach is sensible. Reduce excesses and indulgence. Give up alcohol, cigarettes and other noxious weeds. Drink plenty of water and enjoy lots of fruit, vegetables, pulses and whole grain cereals. Do not be a slave to any diet theory.

Australia has an abundance of good foods and selecting the right combinations, in the right quantities helps ensure good health. At the same time, choosing from a wide variety of food ensures that eating is a pleasurable and healthy experience.

Your body is your home. You must clean up after yourself every day. All the elements you need for a healthy body are found abundantly in nature. A healthy person will not get sick. If you eat your foods as nature has intended for you, they are naturally balanced. Use the whole plant or fruit. Do not throw out the peels or core as they are integral parts.

Chlorophyll contains the light and energy of the sun. It is stored in all plants and fruits that we eat. In reality it is this very light from which we obtain energy to nourish us. Foods highest in chlorophyll are green.

It is important to remember that all fruits and vegetables should be sub ripened and organically grown. The sooner the produce is utilised after harvest, the more alive and nutritious it is. This is why the grasses and sprouts that can be grown all year round in any climate and home are so beneficial.

5. ORGANIC & BIODYNAMIC FOOD

Organic and biodynamic cultivation has been practiced since people first learnt to grow their own food.

Organic produce comes from soil fertilised naturally and grown without the use of chemicals.

Biodynamic farming is a slightly more sophisticated form of organic cultivation, employing various organic preparations for specific purposes.

Some are used to accelerate the development of live enzymes in the soil, others to attract more etheric nutrients from the atmosphere onto the plant's leaves. Unfortunately the conventional method of growing produce today is dependent upon chemicals - chemicals to fertilise the soil, chemicals to control pests and diseases, chemicals to enhance growth and appearance, chemicals to prolong the shelf-life of produce. While this system is profitable, there are numerous problems associated with chemical farming.

Primarily, good food is dependant upon healthy soil, which can only be achieved in accordance with nature's laws. Just as certain bacteria in our intestines are necessary for the proper digestion and assimilation of food, so plants need certain bacteria to enable them to flourish. Soil rife with chemicals becomes so depleted of enzymes and nutrients, that the resulting produce lacks vitamins and minerals, which is then often compensated for by more chemical injection.

Produce that is chemically stimulated and deprived of organic nutrients develops an abnormal cellular structure with an over abundance of carbohydrates (in the form of starches and cellulose) at the expense of cell-building protein. What is most disturbing is, that your body has to cope with the toxic residue that becomes part of this food. Chemically produced toxins are not easily eliminated by your gastrointestinal systems. They build up over time and attack your immune system, leaving you susceptible to allergies, diseases and degeneration. Unlike its chemical counterpart, organic food is nutritious and easy to digest.

6. COLOUR VIBRATIONS

Colour affects the energy centres of the body.

RED
signifies the lower chakras; the sexual organs.
It is blood food, physical, sensual and warming.

ORANGE and YELLOW
aid digestion in the intestines and stomach, relieving gas and
head-aches. It is a radiant energy, full of the sun's glory and is
very cheerful. These foods can loosen mucous and calcium
deposits in the body.

GREEN
is the heart colour and is full of love and peace. It is significant
in growing and balance and can help with all emotional problems.

BLUE
is connected with the lungs and is the link between the heaven
and earth. Fresh air and proper breath controls the nerves.

PURPLE
is inspiring and spiritual food for the mind. It is for
meditation and quiet. It is etheric, electric and full of light.

7. WORLD CRUCIFIXION

Thou shalt not kill
Exodus 20.13

The world is crucified when an animal is crucified ... or a tree ... or any living thing.

Whenever you read of hunting parties, know that you are reading about the seeds of war and hatred. Whenever you see a meat or fish-ridden dining-table, know that you are looking upon one of the seeds of war and hatred - a seed that develops into an ugly weed of atrocity.

When people ask 'Is there likely to be future war?' The answer is 'Yes, until animals are treated as our younger siblings!' They are not at present. We simply use them for our own satisfaction, for food, hauling tremendous loads and for any other purpose we choose. We feel sorry if they suffer. Where there is war anywhere, there is misery, discontent and unhappiness.

A spirit of war can be fostered by the indifference of public opinion. An animal can be killed for food, mutilated in the vivisection chamber for our benefit, beaten and not a word will go forth on the animal's behalf. Many people engage in this or that cruelty because it is sanctioned by public opinion, which permits conventional cruelty ... as long as we are not unconventionally cruel!

Question the question 'What are the animals for? What are you for? Are you to fatten on the sufferings of your younger brethren?'

The feeding of one animal upon another is not a cruel system.

Species learn to give to each other. There is a natural give and take and sharing of energies between kingdoms. This is ecology ... the natural redistribution of energy between kingdoms. It is only our kingdom, the human kingdom, that wants to warehouse energy, to use much more than it needs and to store what it does not, so that the balance of the cycle is disturbed so dramatically. We are all beings in different coats - fur, feathers, scales, skin. It is not a question of whether human life matters more than animal life ... this thinking can lead to 'some human lives may matter more!' All life is sacred. Creatures are here not for our use and abuse, but for our blessing.

Examination reveals that cruelty in its multifarious forms is probably what the world suffers from most at the present time ... and a conscience that is very apathetic about the many wrongs which may be labelled as cruelty. First in the order of demerit are all cruelties to the younger residents of the world - the children, the animals, the brethren of the vegetable kingdom and those too of the mineral kingdom. These helpless creatures are exploited and prostituted for personal and selfish interests. We eat animals, cause pain to them, distort them into ugly forms, demand from them the living of unnatural lives, so that we can be more comfortable. They cannot rebel, still less refuse, because we are stronger. We have that force, and we do not hesitate to use it. Wherever there is such cruelty, there is barbarism, however civilised the country might choose to think itself .

Hunting is a method of war upon the nation of animals. So is vivisection, as is the killing of animals for sport, pleasure, a trophy above the mantelpiece, the fox hunt and fishing. There is a tremendous war against the nation of animals as we force them into slaughter-houses in order that we may have the satisfaction of consuming their flesh.

Perhaps it is an impious irreverence to thank God for our daily bread, if the bread includes the mangled limbs and organs of a once living creature - a creation of the same Being that is being worshipped.

It is not necessary any more to learn and have it cost somebody his or her life; nor for progress to cost the destruction of nature. Even though learning is contained in destruction, the karmic consequences of participating in violence and destruction are a high price to pay.

Everyone of us is responsible for the misery of the poor, the helplessness of the weak and for the helplessness of the average animal. Every individual who becomes a friend of all creatures instead of their enemy and who ceases cruelty in all its forms thus enrols themself in that glowing community which will some day make the world safe, not so much for democracy, as for the universal experience of Reverence, Goodwill and Compassion.

If you feel a pang of compassion for all those innocent cattle slaughtered in this effort… say a brief prayer for them and also for all the people, partners in crime, who are killing themselves in such unwise eating.

The study of Yoga consists of eight facets, one of which observes various abstinences, *Yama*, including non-violence, *Ahimsa*. In its narrow interpretation, it is merely translated as non-killing of people. In its broader sense, it could also include non-violation of animals, things, self and others.

Violence is in the mind of a person. A knife may be used to kill someone, or to pare fruit. *Vedic Rishis,* ancient sages partook of meat in earlier times. From an humanitarian angle, a spiritual viewpoint, a nutritional stance, as well as an ecological per-

spective, meat eating seems to have no justification.
Today, many Yogis do not partake of flesh. One reason some
people follow a vegetarian diet in Yoga is because they do not
wish to kill any developed conscious life for their own sake.
Whilst it is true that everytime we eat something, we kill
something, it is the violence, the pain that we could cause to
animals that we wish to avoid. If you never eat meat or kill
any animals, the animal kingdom all over the globe will wor-
ship you. Wherever you are, they will sense that you are a
person of non-violence and a good friend.

George Bernard Shaw described the bodies of flesh eaters as
graveyards for the carcasses of dead animals. From an humanitarian angle, a meat diet can be eschewed because it is
cruel. Many vegetarians claim that slaughter creates slaughter
within and without. We can be kind to animals by not eating
them.

Observe the animals in a zoo. The carnivores seem to be rest-
less, prowling around, even within their cages, whereas the
vegetarian animals appear so soft and gentle. They look at you
and smile. Animal fat leaves more toxins in the system than
vegetables and is not as conducive to a peaceful mind. However, other factors also need to be considered. One can be a
vegetarian and violent and cruel to the extreme, or a non-
vegetarian and yet kind and loving. In India, for centuries and
generations, there are communities that have lived totally on
vegetarian food. Many *Brahmins* (high caste Hindus) have
been totally vegetarian - they are non-violent but not necessarily spiritual. Jains, totally vegetarian, are one of the most
materialistic communities in India. Eating meat and non-
vegetarian food gives some release to violence (which could
perpetuate violence - *karma*). What you might like to consider
is that if you are violent and your food is vegetarian, then your
violence will have to find some other way of expression.

24

There are some people who release their violence through hunting, or fishing but are otherwise friendly and loving people, and there are also some vegetarian business people whose release of violence becomes the search for wealth and power.

Cultivate the perception of the holiness of all things. Be willing to say "That is Life, we must not harm it." "Those are our fellow humans, we must not destroy them" and mean it. Recognize the rights of the Earth. This attitude creates compassion and acts of kindness, without which the world becomes cold and barren, mechanical and random at the same time ... and this creates experiences of alienation and acts of violence. We shall come to honour all of Life – sooner or later. This is natural ... it connects us with the basic energy of the soul. Our choice lies in (i) when that will happen, and (ii) the quality of experience we have as we learn.

Eat with awareness. Food cannot make you spiritual, but if you are spiritual, your food habits will change.

8. WHAT THE HUMAN ANATOMY & PHYSIOLOGY TELLS US

Structurally and functionally, we are vegetarian animals, in the same class as the primates, the higher apes, such as gorillas, chimpanzees or orang-outangs.

The similarities are interesting to investigate.

Like the higher species of apes, human saliva is alkaline, containing ptyalin to digest carbohydrates. The saliva in carnivores is acidic.

The lower jaw of the human being moves up and down, as well as from side to side, like in the primates. The jaw of the carnivore moves only up and down.

We do not really have fangs, like the carnivores have for biting into flesh. Our so-called canine teeth (incisors) - a misnomer - are not truly canine, like dog's teeth. They are not significantly longer than other teeth. Perhaps we are not constituted to prey upon animals, bite into their flesh or rip apart their bones.

We are made for more gentle manoeuvres in gathering our food. Hands of the human being, like those of apes seem meant for plucking foods such as fruits, vegetables, leaves, flowers, bark, shoots etc. and not for tearing flesh. We do not have claws.

Gastric secretions in human beings are acidic - so are those of the carnivore. However, the stomach of a carnivore has four times as much acid. This strong acid medium is needed to digest a highly proteinous flesh diet.

In human beings, the small and large intestine measures approximately four times the length of ones height. This is similar to that of primates. However, in carnivores, it measures the same as the body's length.

The liver and kidneys of the carnivore are proportionately larger than those in the human being, to handle the excessive nitrogenous waste residue from a flesh diet.

The liver of a carnivore secretes a much larger quantity of bile into the gut, to deal with a high-fat, flesh diet.

These convince us in favour of vegetarianism, for the human constitution. However, just 'any old' vegetarian diet is not alright for our systems. For example, the human body does not have several stomachs, such as ruminants (the cow). Human beings do not chew the cud, as the cow does and therefore cannot live off pasture lands.

Primates are frugivores - the gorilla has a diet with approximately 15% fruit, the chimpanzee's diet consists of approximately 67% fruit and the orang-outang has approximately 50% fruit. In addition to fruit, human beings, like primates need some vegetables, shoots, flowers, grains and seeds.

8.1 ADAPTABILITY OF THE HUMAN SYSTEM

The human system does adapt itself to a non-vegetarian diet, but this is not without certain drawbacks. Eskimos, for example, may live on reindeer and seal meat... however, they die early, their life span being about 30 years. Only in the last 50 years has their life span increased because of the intervention by the Caucasian with health and medical treatments.

We have domesticated a few animals for their dairy produce, and in Ayurveda, milk is considered a 'whole food.' However, it may be relevant to bear in mind that no adult animal drinks any other animal's milk, neither do animals naturally continue to drink milk after they have been weaned. Chinese and Japanese vegetarians do not have an intake of any dairy produce and maintain excellent health on a vegetarian diet that excludes dairy foods.

Fresh fruit, leafy and other vegetables, seeds, nuts, cereals and legumes are more easily and profitably utilised, digested, assimilated and absorbed in the human system. Milk when heated is digested better. Cold milk presents more difficulty for the system.

8.2 CHOLESTEROL VERSUS CHLOROPHYLL

Current research increasingly incriminates a flesh diet for creating pathological disturbances in the human body.

Animal fats are a well-known cause of an increase in cholesterol in the blood. This increase often results in a narrowing of the inner walls of the arteries by fatty deposits, known as arteriosclerosis. When this happens in coronary arteries, the blood supply to the heart muscle itself may be affected, causing a heart attack. When several major arteries and arterioles develop arteriosclerosis, blood pressure generally increases. With high blood pressure, several pathological conditions soon develop in various organs, as it precedes the degeneration of internal organs and is associated with old age and chronic disease. Cerebral haemorrhage too can occur, resulting in paralysis.

More than 50% of all meats produce saturated fats and cholesterol. As even the leanest of meat has some fat in it, persons suffering from cardio-vascular disorders can question a flesh diet. Non-flesh foods, with the exception of eggs, hydrogenated oils and dairy products have no cholesterol-producing fats. Coconut oil, even though it is high in saturated fats, has no cholesterol.

Cardiologists now increasingly advise their patients against meat. As early as 1961, the Journal of American Medical Association conceded that a strict vegetarian diet could prevent 97% of coronary occlusions. Dr Donald Ross, Director of Surgery of the National Heart Hospital London in 1976, all those years ago advocated a study of vegetarian communities, since the incidence of heart diseases in them was much lower than in non-vegetarian communities. He advised his patients to halve their meat intake, cautioning at the same time for restrictions in dairy fats and also advised them to double their vegetarian intake. Dr Ross also proposed the possibility that the human race had not yet adapted to meat protein and in fact believed that atheroma - the patchy degeneration of the walls of large arteries in which fat-like plaques appear, could be a process of the body's rejection of meat proteins taken over a long period of time.

Gall-stones are usually composed of cholesterol. Hence, the less one takes of animal fat, the less likely one is to suffer from stones forming in the gall-bladder (Cholesterolosis).

Natural eating suggests that chlorophyll which is present in leafy and other greens, be eaten in large enough quantities to keep the bloodstream free of cholesterol deposits, so that neither thrombii nor clots form in the blood, nor are the arteries affected. Vitamins C and P, derived from uncooked (actually speaking sun-cooked) fruits and vegetables, including the inner rind of citrus fruits are also nature's anti-thrombosis agents. Vitamin C is important for inter-cellular respiration, fighting infections and healing inflammations. In fact, one of the arguments of Dr Linus Pauling, the champion advocate of Vitamin C in mega dosages is that once human beings lived mainly on vegetables and fruits, consuming up to three grams of Vitamin C daily. Later with the invention of fire and also with human beings becoming hunters and flesh-eaters, their intake of Vitamin C was greatly reduced; the aftermath being a loss of health and vigour. Flesh eaters please note that meat generally lacks in Vitamin C.

8.3 VEGETARIAN DIET SPARES KIDNEYS

Another drawback of flesh eating is the high uric acid content in meat. In the last throes of death, all animals produce acids in their tissues. These are not drained off with blood. Lamb, beef, pork and mutton contain about 14 to 16 grams of uric acid per pound of meat. Human kidneys, not being made for the excretion of fleshy toxins, do not easily cope with excreting more than 7 grams of uric acid per day. Is it any wonder then, that large flesh eaters, who consume more than 250g of meat per day, overload their kidneys? This may result in kidney stones, or inflammation in kidney tissue to start with and kidney failure in the long run. Dialysis and surgical transplants do not solve the problems of an increase in kidney diseases.

Research has also shown that the body of the flesh eater also has to eliminate tissue wastes in the meat, which the kidney of the animal would have excreted, had it not been slaughtered. Nephritis (inflammation of the kidneys) is often the result of these excess fleshy wastes. The Seventh Day Adventist doctors who advocate vegetarianism, rightly feeling that a meatless diet spares the kidneys, have often seen that meat acts like a poison to Bright's disease (degeneration of the kidneys) or nephritis patients. In cases that indicate large amounts of albumin in the urine, patients are advised to be on a diet free of all meat, fish, fowl and eggs. This results in a clear urine sample within a couple of weeks. Uric acid also contributes to other troubles such as gout and to a lesser extent, all types of fibrositis, neuritis and neuralgia, including the formation of lumbago and sciatica, arthritis and other inflammatory conditions of the joints.

8.4 MEAT AND CANCER

Meat being low in fibre is another drawback for the flesh eater. It lacks the cellulose or roughage absolutely necessary in a human diet, without which bowels do not move properly, resulting in constipation. Unfortunately, some people think it is alright even if the excreta is voided once a day or even once in 2-3 days, and do not think that constipation is a health problem. However, those who know better, raise a cautionary finger against constipation, calling it 'the fertile mother of many diseases.' Compare the human system again to the organism of our arboreal ancestors, the apes. They eliminate faeces at least twice a day. So must we.

Cancer of the bowel is on the increase in non-vegetarian diet countries, where constipation is also rife. Bowel cancer has overtaken lung cancer in Australian males as the No.1 cancer-killer, where about 130kg of beef per head is consumed annually . Dr Alan Long, writing for 'The Vegetarian' magazine of the U.K. says that 'Intestinal flora of vegetarians differ from flesh-eaters'; they contain more aerobic bacteria. The flesh-eaters' anaerobic bacteria include bacteriodes containing the enzyme 7-alpha-dehydroxylase, which converts components in the bile juices into deoxycholates, known to be carcinogenic in animals. Concentration of deoxycholates in the faeces relates with the prevalence of colonic cancer.' A survey published as early as 1973 in the Journal of the National Cancer Institute compared the faeces of people on a normal high-protein high-fat US. diet, with those of vegetarians, Seventh Day Adventists and recent Chinese and Japanese immigrants. Excretion of corprostano and corprostanone (which are products of degradation of cholesterol) and of total and degraded bile acid was higher in the flesh-eating group, which bore out earlier contentions. Low-residue diets (deficient in fibre) with correspondingly prolonged transit-times (constipation) and greater opportunities for the action of the 7-alpha-dehydroxylases, were incriminated in 1971 by Dr Burkitt - Reports in 'Gut' Journal in 1969 and in the British Journal of Cancer in 1973, remark that rates of mortality from cancer of the colon relate to consumption of animal protein.

Appendicitis and Haemorrhoids (commonly known as piles) arise because of constipation, whether latent or patent.

8.5 AND DIABETES TOO!

Diabetes is generally associated with too much intake of refined carbohydrates - ie. too much starch and sugar. Often a
high-protein meat diet is recommended to diabetic patients,
under the notion that this would not tax the pancreas to se-
crete insulin, because with an increase in meat intake, the
carbohydrate intake would *ipso facto* decrease. Here the sur-
mise is correct, but it is a very myopic view of the total metabolism.

A study by a medical team lead by Prof. S.P. Verma, Associate
Professor of Medicine at the Maulana Azad Medical College,
New Delhi, has found that the fibre content of vegetables acts
as a protection against diabetes in many cases. At a seminar as
far back as the 23rd of October 1975, on 'Diabetes and Cardiovascular diseases', Dr Verma said that the best way to reduce
the chances of 'getting' diabetes was to eat more vegetables
and unpolished cereals.

Meat constipates - hence it dams excretion, throwing an extra
burden upon the kidneys and the liver, the two important
depurative organs, which are often involved in the origin of
diabetes. It seems that a better treatment to help a diabetic
would be to keep them on a vegetarian diet that includes
whole grain cereals, sprouted legumes, plenty of non-starchy
vegetables, leafy greens and some fruits. Excluding mangoes,
and in some cases, bananas and grapes, most fruit can be eaten
by diabetics. In fact, papaya, oranges, grapefruit, tamarind,
apples, peaches, plums and pears are often specially prescribed for diabetics.

A detailed study of diabetes reveals that it is not only an ex-
cess-carbohydrate disease, but it can be a high-protein or even
high-fat disease.

Because of the high incidence of fat in meat, often flesh eating can result in obesity. Dr O.S. Parrett, M.D. has pointed out that with fat people, some fat infiltrates the tissues of the liver. The liver is the store-house of glycogen (liver carbohydrate). In obese people, extra, useless fat cells in the liver impede the healthy function of the liver cells, resulting in poor storage of sugar and starch in the liver and thereby overloading the blood with sugar. The kidneys now have the job of eliminating this sweet burden in the bloodstream, thus sugar makes its appearance in the urine. Thus, in the cases of obese diabetics, perhaps the fault may not lie in the pancreas but with the liver and often a cure results with weight-reduction.

With respect to the prescription of a meat diet for patients, Dr Parrett explains that 'Food to be avoided in diabetes are starches and sugars in excess. When the blood which normally carries a maximum of 120 units of sugar, reaches 175 or so, there is a spill-over of sugar into the urine through the kidneys. We then seek a diet for the patient that yields its carbohydrates as slowly as possible, lest the blood stream too quickly reaches the spill-over level and it appears in the urine on the surface. Meat, which is mostly protein with little carbohydrate (glycogen) would seem to answer this dietary need admirably, except for two important reasons.

These are :

1. The diabetic has to get rid of nitrogen and sulphur wastes of meat protein metabolism, and

2. In meat are the tissue toxins of the slaughtered animal, which are ingested by the diabetic when they eat meat. As it is, even the diabetic system of the vegetarian is usually burdened with toxins, thus the system of the non-vegetarian would be all the more loaded, increasing

the risk of acidosis.'

Dr Parrett suggests a diet program of low-proteins for the diabetic. He also recommends low-starch vegetables which add carbohydrates slowly to the blood stream. He considers tomatoes ideal, because of their low-starch and high vitamin and mineral content.

In his book 'Diabetes : Its Causes and Treatments', Dr Andrew Gold suggests a vegetarian diet, because he has noticed that the ingestion of butchered meat increases the toxaemic condition underlying the diabetic state and reduces sugar tolerance. On the other hand, the non-flesh, non-stimulating and especially unified vegetarian diet promotes and increases sugar tolerance.

9. HEALTHY REASONS
FOR BEING VEGETARIAN

Many of our evolutionary ancestors were hunters and we have the biological ability to eat just about anything. However if you eat your vegetables, you'll live longer and be healthier and kinder to your purse and to the earth. There are tremendous physical benefits from being vegetarian. In about three months after no longer having meat in your diet, you will notice that you are suddenly more supple. The consequences of no longer eating meat are that your joints will seem to move more freely.

Animal food is dead matter. Anything that is dead will immediately start decomposing and be unfit for eating. When a piece of flesh is cut from a body, it decays, whereas a vegetable is still a living organism. Eat half a potato, cut the other half into ten pieces, plant them and they will yield ten potato plants. On the other hand, with a goat that is cut into ten pieces ... think about it!

Meat takes a long time to digest and the energy one wastes in digesting meat is in many cases more than one gains from it. That's why meat needs to be cooked for so long. If it is left undigested, it starts decomposing and fermenting in the system.

A bean has life in it after several months and some beans and seeds have life in them even after hundreds and thousands of years. To address the concern about vegetarians and enough protein, be assured that it can be had in an easily assimilated form from:
- pulses or legumes, (lentils, peas and beans)
- seeds
- soy products - Tofu & Tempeh (fry lightly)
- grains like Quinoa – (cook as you would rice)

- milk products and vegetables
- Wheat germ (add to cereals & drinks)

A vegetarian diet can also be unwise when it is ill-disciplined and unhealthy. Many vegetarian products are also poisonous to the human system, for instance, cigarette smoking, alcohol, tea, coffee and cocoa which contain harmful alkaloids such as theine, caffeine and theobromine, which are also not "*sattwic*", purifying. Although I am loath to denigrate chocolate, in all fairness, it is made from cocoa butter or vegetable fat which are both high in fat. (Cocoa is separated into cocoa powder (no fat) and cocoa butter when making good quality chocolate. These two are re-combined. When making compound chocolate eg for Yule chocolates and Easter eggs, cocoa powder is combined with vegetable fat. Coca cola contains caffeine and therefore can be addictive. It is also reputed to contain *nux vomica*, a seed from which strychnine is derived. All these items are non-flesh items!

Then there is the problem of refined carbohydrates. Refined sugar, which is chemically speaking 99% sugar, is devoid of all vitamins and minerals originally contained in sugar cane, from which it is made. Not only does it contribute to dental cavities and diabetes, but also to osteoporosis and arthritis. Although sugar is chemically neutral, it is acidic in our system and may cause hyperacidity and peptic ulcers. According to Professor John Yudkin, it also leads to heart disease, as much as animal fats do. Moreover, a research project in USA has traced the connection between anterior poliomyelitis and excess sugar intake. Links between hyper-sucrophagy - too much sugar-intake and psychological disturbances have also been established. For some years of his life, Adolf Hitler was a vegetarian, under medical advice. However, he was fond of too much sugar, putting sugar in everything he ate or drank. Some nutritionists are of the opinion that he was sugar-drunk, which affected his psyche!

It is also noticed that even with children, hyper-sucrophagy tends to make them peevish and cantankerous. We all need sugar. However, it should come from naturally sweet fruits. If these are not easily available, dried fruits are a good substitute.

'Curry-kidney' is a term coined for the people whose kidneys are damaged by the eating of hot chillies. These act as an irritant to the mucous lining of the gastro-intestinal tract. Although high in Vitamin C, their demerit lies in the fact that they set the inner walls of the alimentary canal 'aflame', their irritating factor similarly cauterising or scorching the cells of the liver and the kidneys.

Garlic and onions have been variously ascribed with the virtues of lowering blood pressure, disinfecting the bowel and curing tuberculosis and are therefore in the light of a health-promoting view on diet, to be included. However, not to the extent that one smells of them.

Eat wisely, for adequate fuel, health, well-being, repair of tissues, mental agility, concentration, mental peace and sundry other factors which include enjoyment and pleasure.

In summary; meat:
- is not palatable. Whatever taste it seemingly has, is that of salt and spices.

- is not nutritious, in the sense that whole-wheat bread, or an apple is nutritious. While providing protein and fat it also has harmful acids, cholesterol etc.

- may provide some iron, calcium, phosphorus but there are far better vegetable sources to obtain these minerals and the other minerals which meat lacks.

• Although dairy products do have some animal fats and proteins, there is proof that these definitely contribute to the growth of children, especially. Uric acid is absent from milk and some research actually attributes anti-cholesterolaemic virtues to yoghurt and buttermilk. The diet of the Masai tribes is predominantly one of animal blood and fat, yet these people are remarkably immune to heart disease. This is attributed to their open air living and to their walking long distances. However, many researchers propose that the inclusion of home-made curds - yoghurt in their diet is per haps a contributing factor to their immunity. As per the claims made from the study conducted by Dr Mann and Dr Anna Spoerry of the African Research Foundation, 'The Masais' cholesterol level dropped more if they ate more curds.' Dr Mann is of the opinion that some of the bacteria in yoghurt produces a substance which blocks or inhibits the liver's own cholesterol production.

Vegetarian cuisine can be tasty, low in fat, high in protein, complex carbohydrates and fibre, rich in vitamins and miner- als. You can save time and money, lose weight and have healthy, nutritionally balanced, tasty meals with a difference ... if you know how. Vegetarian eating makes sense! With the rotation of grains, seeds, nuts and pulses and using no animal products (no dairy or eggs) your eating plan can also be suitable for low tolerance and allergy diets. Choose to make your diet free of yeast, M.S.G, added sugar, preservatives, chemicals and pesticides, artificial colourings or flavourings where possible. Use low salt and organically or bio-dynami- cally grown produce where possible, then cook in stainless steel or glass (aluminium has been linked with Alzheimers' disease) ... and you have one of the pillars for the foundation of outstanding health and vitality ... that still tastes delicious.

10. MACROBIOTICS

Macrobiotics is a dietary system of organically grown wholefoods that attempts to balance the principles of yin and yang, which is regarded as present in various foods in different proportions.

An Australian-Italian, American trained, very successful and skilled chiropractor and keen Yoga student first introduced me to a way of life from Japan, called Macrobiotics, in 1973. He was vegetarian, skinny as a reed and had a beautiful hungry Afghan hound named "Taj Mahal" - also vegetarian! Shaggyshoes, our Old English Sheepdog was double Taj's girth ... then again, maybe it was more than the name and size of the hound ... perhaps it was seeing Taj devour a wedge of watermelon, skin and all, that I realized that this dog was hungry and gave him some *Basmati* rice and *dhal* - only to be tiraded about eating white rice. He regaled about the properties of brown rice - with its seven outer layers of bran and vitamins, all of which are removed in the processing to obtain white rice! In the course of events, Dr. Cherki explained how simple food, good food had changed and regenerated his life.

Georges Ohsawa, the Japanese father of Macrobiotics and his wife had revolutionized Japanese and world eating habits. Subsequently, streams of people conducted and participated in seminars on macrobiotics at our previous yoga centre in Melbourne (Australia): the most memorable were the Okiyogaites; Ann Wigmore, wheatgrass specialist; Jayne Sunbird; and the then Professor Curtis Shears, author of Nutritional Science and Health Education who led a fourteen-day intensive workshop called 'Nutrition in Practice' for health educators. In the mid seventies, brown rice, lentils and the value of eating grains and vegetables was all the go! Some of it was very controversial : no water was drunk in a strict macrobiotic eating plan and fruit was kept to a minimum. This, I could never ever agree with and it has now undergone modification. Over the years, I have combined some macrobiotic concepts with my very biased Ayurvedic principles of eating. The only thing that I feel conscience stricken about sometimes is that I have not done more to bring to the notice of the public and show practically what really can be done for suffering humanity with simple dietary education that can be used in every ordinary home. However, this will help.

11. YIN & YANG - BALANCE IN THE BODY

Yin and Yang are a set of interdependent passive (thought of as feminine, negative, intuitive) and active (thought of as masculine, positive, intellectual) philosophical principles of nature. In Chinese, Yin means inertia, darkness. Yang means dynamism, light. In Taoism and Confucianism they are represented by two interlocked curved shapes within a circle, one white and one balck, with a spot of the contrasting colour within the head of each.

Yin and Yang exist to teach us the connection between food and life.

The process which tends to concentrate energy is called centripetal force. It's counterpart is the process that moves an element towards de-materialization and into a loss of its physical cohesion, called centrifugal force.

Yin is centrifugal, passive and receptive. It is space, the moon, cold. It is the water which enters everywhere and assumes all forms. It is feminine. That which is expanding is becoming Yin. Fear is Yin. Water is Yin. Ice is Yin.

Yang is centripetal, active, creative, energetic. It is the sun, fire. It is Time contracted in consciousness. It is masculine. That which is contracting is becoming Yang. Cooking a vegetable over fire is 'Yangising' it. Fire, being Yang, makes the vegetable shrink by evaporating most of its water. If you compare a vegetable fresh from the market with another that has been cooked, the former is Yin and the latter is Yang. Fire has made the difference in a matter of a few seconds.

To reverse the process, add water or any Yin liquid, to change Yang to Yin - a few drops of lemon to a salad, tahini for sauce.

Soya sauce, is a yang liquid, too strong to take in pure form over tempura or vegetables.

One can change anything into Yin or Yang by using only fire or water.

That which is physically light is yin, and that which is heavy is Yang.

Red, orange and yellow are Yang, they tend to approach us. Blue, purple and green keep their distance, or seem to recede and are Yin.

A high-pitched sound is Yin. It rises in centrifugal, expansive movement. A low sound is Yang, as is the voice of a deep baritone.

An apple is compact, not as juicy and grows in colder climates and is Yang. A watermelon, by comparison is bigger and juicier, grows in a warmer climate than the apple and is Yin.

Any vegetable that grows deep in the ground is more or less Yang. Carrots, potatoes and turnips are more Yang than asparagus, which reaches its full height in a few days. Above the ground, anything that grows rapidly and upward is often very Yin. That which grows close to the ground and slowly is more Yang. This explains how Time can make things Yang.

Tropical fruits are Yin; their potassium content is very high. Strawberries and apples are more Yang, they have less potassium and more sodium. Knowing that potassium is Yin and sodium is Yang, the balance everyone is looking for is easy to find. It is of course, different for every individual, varying with (among other things) climatic conditions and the amount of activity.

Quantity also makes a difference. It is preferable to eat a small amount of Yin than a great deal of balanced food.

Balance between Yin and Yang means the best possible health of body and mind. To understand Yin, we must study Yang, compare them with each other and also discover their interrelationships in nature. We know that according to the law of the universe, Yin produces Yang and Yang produces Yin. Many people require coffee in the day. Coffee is very Yin - it produces instant Yang. The person who does not understand proper balance and drinks a dozen cups of coffee a day just to keep herself going is almost a mechanical person. It is the same with athletes who must drink enormous amounts of liquid in order to finish a game - a basketball player is often 10 pounds lighter after a game.

Nature nourishes human beings, who return to her the seed she requires for every new season. She serves us unconditionally throughout our lifetime. We are her legitimate and natural children and she is our irreplaceable mother who possesses no favourites among her offspring. She gives abundantly to whomever wishes to drink and eat. Her table is dressed with the same cloth for poor and rich alike. Her rich gold and silver tableware is displayed in bright and natural settings amongst water and soil. Her capital is infinite, her humility never discussed; she gives without expecting a thing in return.

To become a human is to undertake the adventurous journey from the biological to the spiritual. Human beings are first of all biological in entity. Chlorophyll is transformed into our blood. This transmutation precedes all higher activity. What we eat changes into our blood, thoughts, action, speech. Everything we eat today becomes tomorrow's unique adventure.

12. SEAWEED

The ocean is a wonderful healing environment full of rich minerals and trace elements that your body needs. Seaweed and algae are valuable vegetables that have long been neglected in many diets. Here the plant structures are simple and the sun's energy is readily released with minimal digestion. Seaweed is an excellent source of iodine that is not readily available in most foods. Iodine helps build a healthy thyroid gland and minerals help build strong and healthy structures. Be sure to rinse off any excess sea salt on the seaweed before soaking.

From the 1960s - 70s, seaweeds have been farmed, and the alginates extracted are used in convenience foods, ice-cream, and animal feed, as well as in toothpaste, soap, and the manufacture of iodine and glass.

KELP powder can be substituted for salt in soups and casseroles and used daily.

NORI is pressed sheets of fine seaweed. Excellent for rolling up Nori-rolls (Norimaki) which are filled with rice and your favourite fillings. Also used cut in fine strips as a garnish in soups or salads.

HIJIKI soaked in water has a marvellous flavour of the sea and can be used in any salad.

DULSE can be eaten as it is, dried, or may be soaked and used in sauces and soups for seasoning, like Kelp. Scottish and Irish people have used this seaweed for centuries. Check for seashells!

WAKAME and KOMBU must be soaked and chopped. They

are thicker in texture and are great in blended soups.

SPIRULINA ALGAI, an amazing energy food and excellent source of chlorophyll and protein (about 60%) was used by the ancient Aztecs in Mexico. It grows profusely on fresh water ponds and home cultivation is possible. It can be purchased in powdered form and can be sprinkled over soups and meals or added to smoothies and juices.

13. WATER

8 glasses a day keeps fat away

Your body is made up of more than half water. We are constantly needing to cleanse and regenerate all our organs and cells. It is best to drink freely one hour before or two to three hours after any given meal, but not during. It is also important to bathe, shower or swim at least once a day to open up the pores of your skin. Always remember to rinse off with cold water after a hot shower, sweat or steam bath. This will prevent dirt and pollution entering open pores and improve muscle tone.

In many parts of the world, our water has become polluted, contaminated, chemicalized and is no longer safe to drink. The best water to use for all good preparation is spring or distilled water. Expose it to sunlight for several hours. There is plenty of organic water in fresh food. Soaking dried or fresh fruit, vegetables or seeds adds nutrients to the 'dead water'.

Incredible as it may sound, water is quite possibly the single most important catalyst in losing weight and keeping it off. Although most of us take it for granted, water may be the only true 'magic potion' for permanent weight loss.

Water suppresses the appetite naturally and helps the body metabolise stored fat. Studies have shown that a decrease in water intake will cause fat deposits to increase, while an increase in water intake can actually reduce fat deposits.

Here's why: The kidneys can't function properly without enough water. When they don't work to capacity, some of their load is dumped onto the liver.

One of the liver's primary functions is to metabolise stored fat into useable energy for the body. But, if the liver has to do some of the kidney's work, it can't operate at full throttle. As a result, it metabolises less fat; more fat remains stored in the body and weight loss stops.

Drinking enough water is the best treatment for fluid retention. When the body gets less water, it perceives this as a threat to survival and begins to hold onto every drop. Water is stored in extracellular spaces (outside the cells). This shows up as swollen feet, legs and hands.

Diuretics offer a temporary solution at best. They force out stored water along with some essential nutrients. Again, the body perceives a threat and will replace the lost water at the first opportunity. Thus the condition quickly returns.

The best way to overcome the problem of water retention is to give your body what it needs - plenty of water. Only then will stored water be released.

If you have a constant problem with water retention, excess salt may be to blame. Your body will tolerate sodium only in a certain concentration. The more salt you eat, the more water your system retains to dilute it.

But getting rid of un-needed salt is easy - just drink more water. As it's forced through the kidneys, it takes away excess sodium.

Water acts as a solvent in the body and the more pure it is, free from inorganic minerals, dissolved heavy metals, softeners and pollutants the more body toxins can be let into it and also the more organic nutrients it can carry to the body's cells. Other fluids like coffee, tea, fruit juices, milk and other liquids don't really replace the body's need for water.

Every living cell requires water, just as it does nutrients and oxygen. Water regulates all bodily functions and is essential for the removal of wastes especially from the lymphatics which act as the cell lever.

The overweight person needs more water than the thin one. Larger people have large metabolic loads. Since we know that water is the key to fat metabolism, it follows that the over-weight person needs more water.

Water helps rid the body of waste. During weight loss, the body has a lot more waste to get rid of - all that metabolised fat must be shed. Again adequate water helps flush out the waste.

Water helps to maintain proper muscle tone by giving muscles their natural ability to contract and by preventing dehydra-tion. It also helps to prevent the sagging skin that usually follows weight loss - shrinking cells are buoyed by water, which pumps the skin and leaves it clear, healthy and resilient.

There are no enzymes in rocks. Our trace mineral consump-tion comes from the living foods we eat such as vegetables, fruits, grains etc. These foods release organic minerals ie. they can be absorbed and used by the body.

Inorganic minerals, like water with a high iron content is no cure for anaemia (low iron). Also osteoporosis (low calcium in the bones) is not cured by drinking water high in inorganic calcium. Inorganic minerals are difficult for the body to as-similate and eliminate and eventually accumulate in the joints etc. causing pain and spurs.

Water can help relieve constipation. When the body gets too little water, it siphons what it needs from internal sources. Result? Constipation. But, when a person drinks enough water, normal bowel function usually returns.

So far, we've discovered some remarkable truths about water and weight loss:
- The body will not function properly without enough water and can't metabolise stored fat efficiently.
- Retained water shows up as excess weight.
- To get rid of excess water you must drink more water.
- Drinking water is essential to weight loss.

Whilst some evidence suggests that drinking cold water can actually help burn calories, and therefore water should preferably be cold - it's absorbed into the system more quickly than warm water. However, the Ayurvedic perspective is that cold water dampens the metabolic fire *Agni*. When *Agni* is low, food is partially digested, creating *Aama*, toxic waste ... and is not recommended.

To utilise water most efficiently during weight loss, follow this schedule :

Morning	: 1 litre consumed over a 30-minute period.
Noon	: 1 litre consumed over a 30-minute period.
Evening	: 1 litre consumed between five & six o'clock.

If possible it is best not to drink with meals. Water will dilute the enzymes required for correct digestion.

Drink water up to half an hour before and not sooner than one hour after a meal (while food is digesting).

When the body gets the water it needs to function optimally, its fluids are perfectly balanced. When this happens, you have

reached the 'breakthrough point'.
This means
- Endocrine-gland function improves.
- Fluid retention is alleviated as stored water is lost.
- More fat is used as fuel because the liver is free to metabolise stored fat.
- Natural thirst returns.
- There is a loss of hunger almost overnight.

Remember
- Nutritional Stress arises if you eat a poison (junk food);
- Physical Stress arises if you hurt yourself;
- Mental Stress arises if you get angry etc.

You create a shock at cellular level and will need water to replace the water loss from the blood stream being held as fluid retention.

If you stop drinking enough water, your body fluids will be thrown out of balance again and you may experience fluid retention, unexplained weight gain and loss of thirst. To remedy the situation you'll have to go back and force another 'breakthrough'.

14. FASTING

Fasting is the practice of going without food. It can be undertaken as a religious observance (devout Muslims go without food between sunrise and sunset during the month of Ramdan), a sign of mourning, a political protest ('hunger strike'), or for slimming purposes.

Fasting is a most natural method of self healing. It gives the body a chance to catch up on digestive functions and give energy to other important parts, eg, heart and head centres. True fasting is either a dry fast or a water fast (spring or distilled is best). It is always best to take into consideration your body's present condition and diet.

Fasting and Starvation are not the same. Starvation is draining, depleting, exhausting. It always guarantees weight loss! But, it brings about premature ageing, which is cellular damage. It is a poor choice for weight loss.

Exercise is a very important part of a healthy life. Without proper exercise good elimination is impossible. Oxygen is utilized by the whole body. Breathing exercises and Yoga are excellent. If you do not use your body, you will surely lose it. If you want to burn body fat, you must combine reducing the amount of fat you're putting into your mouth (how much chocolate did we have last week?) with exercise. Exercise is not only about losing weight. You cannot get lean, strong and healthy without exercise.

Fasting is cleansing, energising, exhilarating. It brings about rejuvenation & cell repair. *Upavasa*, fasting which is sometimes counted as one of the practices of self-discipline *niyama*, is also often considered to be a possible obstacle, *vighna*, to spiritual progress. Take your time in detoxifying. It is not a race. A moderate transition is much more desirable.

The *Mahabharata* (XII. 214.4) deems prolonged fasting harmful and instead recommends abstention from eating between breakfast and the evening meal.

The *Gheranda-Samhita* (V.31) specifically mentions that fasting should be avoided in conjunction with the practice of breath control, *pranayama*.

The *Varaha-Upanishad* (II.39) explains that true fasting is the proximity between the individual self, *jiva-atman* and the transcended Self, *parama-atman*, and not the emaciation, *shoshana*, of the body.

Prolonged fasting can be dangerous. The liver breaks up its fat stores, giving the breath a smell of pear drops which indicates a condition known as ketosis, with accompanying symptoms of nausea, vomiting, fatigue, dizziness, severe depression and irritability. Muscles and body tissue become wasted and death eventually results.

HERE ARE SOME IDEAS TO GET YOU STARTED:

Could you consider on the eleventh day after the new or full moon, *ekadasi*, eating fruits and raw milk only? (unpasteurised milk needs to be boiled and then drunk warm).

Could you for a fortnight in a year, consider fasting from your greatest desires? ... giving up the things the mind likes the best?

Could you gradually start eliminating undesirable foods and adding more chlorophyll rich foods?

15. CLEANSING & PURIFICATION

Health, energy, intelligence and emotional stability are all governed by the chemicals, drugs and toxins within the body. This pollution does not go away. Research has shown that drugs and chemicals stay in the body long after they have been consumed causing fatigue, illness and reduced mental energy. As a speaker I have noticed that among the topics that appear to get a good listening, is when I ad-lib about self responsibility for one's own health, and not leaving that responsibility to doctors, who are better informed about disease... and also when I go into some detail describing how to examine body wastes, in particular the colour, odour, composition and frequency of breath, sweat, urine and faeces and to take appropriate measures in cleaning the lungs, skin, kidneys, liver and bowel.

When we start to cleanse our bodies there is an increase of toxic elimination. These toxins could be from years of improper eating habits. Toxins are eliminated through the mouth, ears, skin, lungs, kidneys, intestines and mind. Heavy elimination is not recommended for pregnant or nursing mothers, who should wait till the child is independent after weaning, but can add greens, sprouts and carrot juice to their diets.

Healing crises are expected to occur, during which you may feel weaker. However, after each healing crisis you will feel stronger, as more light and life will radiate through your whole body. When the walls of the intestines are packed with toxic debris it interferes with digestion and assimilation and most people do not assimilate the food they eat. Eventually you will find that your body does not require as much food as you once thought it did.

Ayurveda has five main cleaning practices, known as The *Panchakarma* Treatments. These stem from the principles that health and beauty arise from the circulation of vital life-fluids and appropriate removal of body wastes. They ensure that the body can properly utilise a diet that promotes health and a sense of well-being. They nourish by stimulating the inner resources of the body to maintain health.

The Ayurvedic Treatments are the world's most effective detoxification program to:
• regain health and physical vitality
• rid the body of accumulated toxins
• increase mental energy and think more clearly
• recover enthusiasm for life.

Imbalance of the Ayurvedic constitution, ie body types, *doshas* causes vitiation (contamination) of tissues, *dhatus* and or waste, *malas*.
Medicine, *Kayachikitsa* has two branches:
1. alleviation, *shaman*, which treats the disease without eliminating the *doshas*, the three biological principles, out of the body
2. elimination, *shodhan*, which eliminates vitiated *doshas* out of the body.

Both of these can be achieved by the five-fold therapy in Ayurveda called *Panchakarma*. The five procedures are :
• elimination from upper orifice of alimentary canal, *vaman;*
• from the lower orifice, *virechan;*
• cleaning of the large intestine, bladder etc. *basti;*
• enhrine therapy effective in diseases above the sternal notch, *nasya,*
• to stimulate spleen & liver, *rakta mokshan.*

These treatments are best advised and supervised by Ayurvedic physicians.

15.1 CLEANSING DIET

ON WAKING
A glass of hot water with a squeeze of lemon juice.

BREAKFAST:
Low-sugar fruit, e.g. one grapefruit with outer peel removed, eaten whole.
Fresh banana, slice of pawpaw, an apple.

1 HR BEFORE LUNCH:
Water.

LUNCH:
Steamed vegetables.
Grains, eg. brown rice and possibly legume or tofu (grains soften the cleansing effect a bit; adding the legume or tofu does so even more).

1 HR BEFORE DINNER:
Fresh vegetable juice.

DINNER:
Soup.
Salad with steamed vegetables.

There is no substitute for greens in your diet. Fruit diets are very cleansing but can be too drastic for an overly toxic person. If boils or skin eruptions should happen during fruit fasts (especially citrus) remember to add greens right away.

Eat foods that are lighter and easier to digest before heavier foods. Respect the food chain : water, juice, fruit, sprouts, vegetables, seeds, nuts, grains.

15.2 JUICE FAST

Food which flows in your whole body as pure water, like a river, takes all diseases and empties them into the sea.

• **Approx .25 litre each, depending upon body weight.**
• **Best with organic fruits and vegetables.**
• **Drink immediately after extraction.**
• **Sip slowly.**

6 am
- lemon (optional 1/2 tsp honey / pinch salt) water
8 am
- grapefruit/orange juice (fresh!!!) (3:1)
10 am
- carrot/apple juice (3:1)
12 noon
- grapefruit/cucumber/lettuce juice (5:3:1)
2 pm
- carrot/apple/celery (3:2:1)
4 pm
- green juice (eg carrot/spinach)
6 pm
- V6 / V8: carrot, zucchini, celery, tomato, green pepper, onion, etc. Heated, not boiled, in cool weather. (V means vegetable.)
8pm
- Hot herbal tea according to dosha indications (constitution, conditions, season etc).

15.3 MAJOR CLEANSING CHANNELS

COLON
Maintain:exercise, high fibre diet, water.
Extra help: lemon/honey/salt drink. *Triphala**

URINARY TRACT
Maintain: water, diet low in fat, salt, protein.
Extra help: whey, cell salts.

SKIN
Maintain: water, exercise.
Extra help: brushing (skin), exhalation twice as long as inhalation.

LUNGS
Maintain : complete breath.
Extra help: diaphragmatic breathing with sandbag on chest or back.

* *Triphala*, based on three Ayurvedic miracle fruits:
amla - rejuvenates *Pitta*,
haritaki - rejuvenates *Vata*,
bibitaki - restores *Kapha*,
has a tonic and rejuvenating effect as well as cleansing the intestine. It is available in the form of an Ayurvedic medicine from Ayurvedic practitioners.

Pour boiling water over a tsp of *triphala*, three fruits, powder in a cup, and let stand overnight. In the morning, strain and drink. It's bitter, sour, pungent, astringent ... and at the end, thankfully slightly sweet.

Part Two: Ayurveda, the Science of Life

16. AYURVEDA, THE SCIENCE OF LIFE

Indian cuisine has been designed by the medicine men of old, in contrast to Western cuisine, which is designed by creative chefs. Seeds, roots, stalks, herbs, the bark of a tree etc. are all part of the herbal and preventative medicinal properties of Indian cooking. The base sauce from seeds, stalks, roots and herbs is made first and the food cooked in this sauce, so that it can, with the heat of cooking, add the herbal medicinal qualities to the food. (In Western cooking, the sauce is often added last to the cooked ingredients).

Every culture has had its healers and divine visionaries who have recognised the divine intelligence of the natural world. From the earliest days of human life on this planet, people have derived much of their natural healing systems from their scientific and spiritual customs.

Ayurveda is the ancient medical-counterpart of Yoga from India, dating back to 3,000 BC. Said to be the oldest most complete medical system in the world, the original source of Ayurveda is from the *Atharva Veda* and texts known as the *Samhitas* with comprehensive treatises on health-care and medical procedures. Ancient systems of natural healing look at the whole being. Ayurveda involves the totality of life. It sees human beings as smaller versions of the universe in which everything is interconnected and inter-dependent. Health is not just a smooth functioning body but the total fulfilment of one's personality in harmony with the environment.

Ayurveda approaches herbs through a science of energetics. The properties of herbs are related systematically according to their taste, elements, heating or cooling effects after digestion and other special potencies they may possess.

India's vast knowledge of plant pharmacopoeia is legendary. Indian plants were being traded to other countries at the time of India's ancient Indus Valley civilisation, which existed around 3,000 BC. Meanwhile travellers were taking this same information overland through Tibet into China. Over five thousand years ago, knowledge of India's plant pharmacopoeia was being exchanged throughout the then known civilised world. Indigenous Indian seeds such as coriander have been found in the tombs of Egyptian pharaohs and Indian plants were used by the textile makers of Mesopotamia for the making of dyes.

Around 500 BC, the text and treatise *Charaka Samhita*, was written and compiled by *Charaka*, a student of *Atreya*, who taught and practiced Ayurvedic medicine at *Taxila University*. A remarkable feature of Charaka's great treatise is its theory of classification. The treatise is most exacting in its classification of those living things born of seeds, the plants and trees, sacred, medicinal, culinary, cosmetic, aromatic, which are the laboratory of Ayurvedic medicine.

17. PLANT LABORATORY OF AYURVEDA

17.1 Medicinal plants

After identifying almost 1,500 plants belonging to four types according to their fruits and flowers and whether they are annual or perennials, Charaka then isolated 350 plants useful to Ayurvedic medicine. The medicinal plants are divided into fifty groups, according to the physiological actions of the medicines that can be extracted from them. These fifty groups cover everything from curatives to preventatives and present a sound cross-section of India's medicinal herbs, shrubs and trees: ranging from diuretics, cardiac tonics and plant extracts capable of knitting together bone fractures, to plants that increase fertility both in men and women, bronchodilators, purgatives, digestives and antidotes to poisoning.

Also classified are many of the poisonous actions of Ayurvedic plants, the seasons and times of day when a particular plant's medicinal powers achieve their maximum potency, indicating when it should be collected. Modern science still extracts most of its medicines from plants and yet in this age of galloping information, people know less and less about the medicinal value of plants and herbs.

17.2 Culinary plants

Dietetics form an integral part of Charaka's treatise. Charaka describes the digestibility, nutritional value and medicinal action of several hundred edible and drinkable substances, observing how these substances can be: rendered harmful, or nutritionally enhanced by the way they are prepared or cooked, or by the manner in which they are combined with other foods, or the quantities in which they are taken, or the season and local climate where they are consumed. Edible and potable substances which identify various kinds of legumes, species of cereals, salts, spices, herbs, fish, meats, cooking oils, milk products, drinking water, curatives, tonics, nutrients, medicines and preserves are all present on the shelves and are the basis of household cooking.

I encourage you to make the time for food preparation. Its preparation is meditation in action.

17.3 Cosmetic plants

Most human beings are naturally attracted to beautiful images, although definition of a beautiful image differs vastly depending upon the culture.

In civilised societies beauty is nurtured for commercial gain. When it comes to beauty many people have a tendency to focus on physical appearance, with images of beauty and sex alluring at a superficial level. Images of utopian beauty are used to sell products and services, which you, the media and just about everybody colludes in, encouraging the notion that women have to live up to a utopian idea of perfection. If you are obsessed with physical images of beauty and perfection, you will be certain deep down inside that you will never be attractive enough. In an attempt to live up to these images we forget about inner beauty, intangible, with no defining limits, which ironically is available to us all and a lot easier to attain. Physical beauty is temporary. Wasting your life fixated on trying to become more attractive pays decreasing dividends over time. Real beauty is about being real. It requires an inward focus that is in direct contrast to trying to achieve an external ideal. The beauty myth encourages an external focus rather than an internal appreciation. To chase it is to be perpetually disappointed; its ideals are never met. The image you are trying to achieve is simply a two dimensional illusion, compared to three dimensional reality.

Many Indian women participate in *sola shingar* the sixteen
classical methods of adornment. Ayurveda stresses that
beauty can only emerge through health and through the peri-
odic cleansing of the body necessary for an individual's physical rejuvenation. As a result of this principle, all the plants
from which Ayurveda extracts its cosmetics, perform a medical and purifying function as well: soap substitutes made
from turmeric which possesses antibacterial properties that
disinfect the skin while cleansing it; plants used in hair oils
and shampoos known to have antifungal properties, still others are known to be useful against clogged pores or scalp
infections.

Ayurveda lays strong emphasis on rejuvenation through the
preservation of the body's natural oils, and has evolved an
array of natural oils, skin defoliants to raise a patient's temperature, so toxins can be excreted through perspiration; to
lower the patient's temperature; to close the pores against
external contaminants; some remove stress and fatigue while
softening the skin, others relieve arthritic or rheumatic pain
while helping the body shed dead skin; still others cleanse and
disinfect the skin while acting as aids to the digestive system.
Breath fresheners, lip colourings, dyes that colour the hair
while cleaning the scalp of its sebaceous secretions ... except
for rare exceptions such as treatments made from the precious
saffron plant, most of these cosmetic treatments are available
to any Indian, not just the privileged. As they are natural
products, the chances of unpleasant side effects are much
reduced, especially when compared to those of their chemical
counterparts marketed so aggressively all over the world.

17.4 Aromatic plants

The Charaka treatise emphasises that the senses must be healthy if humans are to experience true well-being. Perfumery is one of India's most ancient and venerated crafts, integrated into daily life, from the ritual to the culinary, from the celibate to the erotic. For instance, certain aromatic gums and flowers made into incense and burned at family altars, during morning and evening devotions echo one of the rules of hygiene created by Ayurveda, requiring the fumigating of chambers with incense, as a disinfectant and against insects. Scented flowers have always been strung into garlands or worn to decorate the hair ... Ayurveda has examined the flowers which give Indians so much pleasure and identified their essential oils; drugs capable of curing headaches, even migraines. Ayurvedic psychiatrists claim that flowers have a tranquillising effect on those suffering from mental agitations. Growing plants encourages people to tend to nature rather than destroy it. The garden and the awareness of it provides medicine to both the body and its senses, as well as to the spirit, and produces that tranquil state without which no person is truly healthy.

18. HISTORIC OVER-VIEW CONTINUES

For the next fifteen hundred years, centuries before the birth of
Islam, at the time of the Queen of Sheba and King Solomon,
the merchants of Asia Minor held the monopoly of western
trade in Indian plants and spices. Ayurvedic science began to
be studied by Arab physicians and Indian medicinal plants
entered the Arab Materia Medica. Those physicians in turn
imparted this information to the physicians of the Arab, Greek
and Roman worlds, whose knowledge would eventually form
the basis of European medicine. All of Europe was searching
for a means to acquire India's spices and plants, absorbing into
its own medical knowledge the information produced by
Ayurvedic medicine. The spice trade even led to the discovery
of America - since Columbus' mission was to find access to the
spices of India ...those fabled spices which could preserve
foods, provide aromatics, cosmetics and produce medicines.

It was the world's tragedy that India began to fragment with
the decay of the Moghul Empire. The great centres of Indian
learning fell apart and scholarship was dispersed by two
centuries of political unrest. The British established their empire in India and for a whole century of British rule, many
Indians colluded with Western thought in despising Indian
scientific learning as native superstition which was the white
man's burden to remove.

It was not until India became independent that Ayurveda
began to regain its reputation as a valid school of medicine.
The Indian government has now opened laboratories for the
clinical testing of Ayurveda's medicinal plants. India's for-
estry departments are studying and growing these plants in
scientific conditions, advised by forest dwellers whose ancestors cultivated forest plants for countless millennia. The

country's botanical gardens are creating and preserving Indian herbaria, so that Ayurvedic physicians have a constant source of medicinal plants. More and more people, both Indians and visitors from the West are now visiting Ayuryedic centres.

19. AYURVEDIC CENTRES TODAY

Treatment centres are based on the cleansing therapies, *Pancha Karma* for detoxifying the body, which Ayurveda holds essential for the regeneration of the body's tissues, muscles and bones. It is both a preventative treatment, even if a patient does not have an obvious medical illness, as well as for medical treatment. Traditional Ayurvedic philosophy holds that the human body must go through this process of detoxification at least once a year to rejuvenate itself and considers these treatments particularly effective for nervous and neurological problems.

A series of emetics, purges, enemas and nasal baths made from prominent Ayurvedic plant extracts are the first step of treatment.

This cleansing process is then followed by inducing sweating through exercise, warming teas and in steam and dry heat baths, where the poisons which can be released through the skin are removed.

The body is then massaged over a period of days with different medicated oils, which are absorbed into the bloodstream where they interact with the body's chemistry. The massage is determined by the energy meridians in the body. Tapping into the universal life force that is in and around all living things, practitioners transmit it to the body via their hands. Strokes, kneading, stretching, pulling, wringing, percussive hand movements, pressure to stimulate and more gentle strokes to relax, deep tissue manipulation and pressure-point stimulation loosens the muscles, improves circulation and cellular waste removal, soothes the nerves, tones the skin and affects deeper organs and tissues, the aura, chakras and the energy body, enhancing emotional, physical and spiritual well-being.

Aromatherapy, reiki, shiatsu and acupressure points all have their origins in Ayurvedic massage, which is like being plugged into a pure, natural source of energy and lit up by its vibration.

For lubrication of the intestine and colonic hygiene, specific herbal decocotions are used. The respiratory system is cleansed and the sense organs nourished through nasal drops, nasal lavage, etc. The patient is fed on a diet in which purity is of particular significance, so the Ayurvedic Centre maintains its own source of water, dairy and beehives, as well as its own vegetable gardens: growing and preserving them for their own well-being and for the well-being of future generations. Indian reverence for plants is unique in that it has an unbroken continuity from prehistory to the present times. The forest represents endless self-regeneration of life; an ecosystem, complete in itself.

In many of the centres physicians cultivate their own gardens of medicinal plants, as well as acquiring herbs from forest dwellers who collect them in the wild.

Ayurvedic centres have their own laboratories where the plants and their mixtures are compounded according to exact prescriptions.

20. THE AYURVERDIC CONSTITUTIONS

The body and the universe constitute the world of relativity, in which mutually dependent opposites exist, each giving meaning to the other.

Seen in terms of five elements, earth, water, fire, air and space, they correspond with five cognitive senses - smell, taste, sight, touch and hearing. Earth and space are the parameters for the atom; variables lie within water, fire and air.

There is also the concept of universal energy, or life force, *prana*, which is the basis of all life, flowing along pathways, rivers or meridians of energy, called *nadis*.

Each individual is born with a unique composition of these elements. When the forces are balanced, the body is healthy; when they are imbalanced, disease follows. Physical symptoms, emotional reactions and spiritual beliefs set alongside social and environmental factors enable us to understand how the energy dynamics of the individual leads to health and harmony.

20.1 *TRI- DOSHAS :* VATA, PITTA, KAPHA

The all-pervasiveness of space and the expansiveness of air make up a force that is linked to the control of movement, the functioning of the nervous system and co-ordination of the functions of different parts of the body and human faculties. *Vata,* wind function is responsible for blood circulation, breathing, excretion, procreation, speech, touch and hearing.

The transformational aspects of fire, *Pitta,* make up the force of heat and energy that control digestion and all biochemical processes in the body. *Pitta* is responsible for bile, digestion, hunger, thirst, vision, heat regulation and intellect. It digests food and converts it into plasma, blood, flesh and muscle, fat, bone, marrow, nerve and brain tissue and reproductive fluids.

The fluidity of water and the cohesiveness of earth make up a force that constitutes the stabilising influence of *Kapha,* which controls the body's fluid metabolism. It lubricates joints and muscles and helps heal.

These three are known as *tri-doshas,* three doshas.

20.2 CHARACTERISTICS OF IMBALANCED DOSHAS

The doshas that predominate in one's mind-body type are the very doshas that are most apt to over-accumulate in the physiology, creating imbalance and health problems. For example, a *vata* type will be the one most likely to suffer from an over-accumulation of *vata*.

Imbalanced Vata
- Dry or rough skin
- Insomnia
- Constipation
- Common fatigue (non-specific cause)
- Tension headache
- Intolerance to cold
- Underweight
- Anxiety, worry

Imbalanced Pitta
- Rashes, skin inflammations
- Heartburn
- Visual problems
- Excessive body heat
- Premature greying, balding
- Hostility, irritability

Imbalanced Kapha
- Oily skin
- Slow digestion
- Sinus congestion
- Nasal allergies
- Obesity
- Lethargy, dullness

20.3 CREATING BALANCE

There are specific recommended health programs designed to re-establish balance and remove the symptoms that may develop when particular doshas are imbalanced. Amongst the various ways to maintain equilibrium, are guidelines in food, philosophy and habits dating back to the sages. These allow us to combine an ancient way of living with a western style of life, mingling in our cooking and attitudes to life.

21. TASTE, *RASA*

Various taste qualities affect the action of *Prana*, 'life-force' in the body. Ordinarily we associate taste with enjoyment and as a means of identification. Ayurveda states that the taste of a herb is not incidental, but an indication of its therapeutic properties. Different tastes possess different effects.

The Sanskrit word *rasa* means 'essence', 'sap', 'appreciation', 'to feel lively'. Taste thus indicates the essence of the plant; that which communicates feeling, which reflects the properties of the sap which invigorates it and is the energising power of taste.

Taste directly affects the nervous system through *Prana*, the life force in the mouth, which is connected to *Prana* in the brain. Through stimulating *Prana*, particularly the gastric nerves, taste affects the digestive fire, *agni*, and enhances the power of digestion. Good taste of food is vitally necessary to awaken *agni* for proper digestion. For this reason bland food may not be nourishing, despite its vitamin and mineral content. Without stimulating *agni*, there is no real power of digestion. Ayurvedic medicine has therefore always included the science of cooking with the right herbs and spices. Together they are part of the field of Ayurvedic herbal science. When sick, you lose your sense of taste and appetite. Lack of taste indicates disease, low *agni*, (digestive fire) and high *ama* (partially digested food which becomes toxic in the body).

Ayurveda recognises six main tastes : Sweet, Sour, Salty, Pungent, Bitter, Astringent :

- **SWEET** is the taste basically of sugars and starches.
  Sugar, sugarcane, glucose, milk, butter, rice, breads, pasta are examples.

- **SOUR** is the taste of fermented or acidic things.
  Yoghurt, lemon, cheese, citrus are examples.

- **SALT** is the taste of salt and alkalis.
  Rock salt, Sea salt, Celtic salt & Black Himalayan salt.

- **PUNGENT** is a spicy or acrid taste and is often aromatic.
  Ginger, chilli, hot peppers, horseradish are some examples.

- **BITTER** is the taste of bitter herbs, like gentian or golden
  seal. Green leafy vegetables, bitter melon, fenugreek, neem,
  tumeric are other examples.

- **ASTRINGENT** has a constricting quality.
  Examples are herbs that contain tannin, like oak bark.
  Beans, lentils, unripe banana and pomegranate are more
  examples.

Taste is the sensory quality that belongs to the element of
water. Plants are the life-form belonging to the element of
water. Though all the six tastes transmit the properties of the
five elements, they are all based on the element of water,
which manifests them. It is only when the tongue is wet that
we recognise taste.

21.1 Relationship between the Six Tastes
& the Five Elements

The Six tastes derive from the Five elements. Each taste is
composed of two elements:
- **Sweet** (taste)   is composed of   earth and water.
- **Sour** (taste)   is composed of   earth and fire.
- **Salty** (taste)   is composed of   water and fire.
- **Pungent** (taste)   is composed of   fire and air .
- **Bitter** (taste)   is composed of   air and space.
- **Astringent** (taste) is composed of   earth and air.

22. ENERGY, *VIRYA*

Through their taste, herbs tend to heat or cool the body. This produces the most basic energising effect upon the system.

The energy or potency of herbs is designated by Ayurveda as **heating** or **cooling**. They are substances that contain respectively the energy of fire, *agni* or water, *soma*.

Through their energy the six tastes fall into two groups:
1. HEATING : pungent, sour and salty, which **cause heat** and increase Pitta.
2. COOLING : sweet, astringent and bitter, which **cause cold** and decrease Pitta.

Energy, *virya*, tells us the effect of a herb on Pitta doṣha.

Pungent tastes, commonly known in hot peppers, chillies, ginger and other hot spices, have a **heating** effect.

Sour or acidic tastes, like citrus or products of fermentation like wine, yoghurt or pickles are **heating**. Fermenting creates combustion which releases heat.

Salt is also **heating**, which can be experienced by the burning sensation it produces on cuts or sores.

Sweet is a cooling taste, as sugar counteracts burning sensations in the body.

Bitter and **cold** are often synonymous, as is experienced in bitter herbs like gentian and golden seal which reduce fever and inflammation.

An **Astringent** taste has a constricting effect, which is the

76

action of something **cold**, like ice and is in such astringent substances as alum, oak bark or witch hazel.

Heating herbs cause dizziness, thirst, fatigue, sweating, burning sensations and they speed up the power of digestion. They increase *Pitta*, but generally decrease *Vata* and *Kapha*. Pungent is the most heating taste, followed by Sour and then Salty.

Cooling herbs are refreshing, enlivening and produce tissue firmness. They are calming and clearing to *Pitta* and to the blood, but generally increase Vata and *Kapha*. Bitter is the most cooling, followed by astringent and then sweet.

Because a person's overall condition can be influenced by affecting the pattern of internal energy of prana that flows through the human body, cool or cold food relieves conditions where there is heat in the body - high fever, bright red cheeks, intense headache, while warm or hot foods relieve cold symptoms - chronic fatigue, pallor, cold limbs. Those which are neither hot nor cold are valued as neutral for their calming effects.

23. STAGES OF DIGESTION

Digestion occurs in three stages, *Kapha*, *Pitta* and *Vata* respectively.

Kapha Stage
The first stage of digestion is in the mouth and stomach; moistening, dominated by the **sweet taste**.

Pitta stage
The second stage of digestion is in the stomach and small intestine; heating, dominated by **sour or acid taste**.

Vata stage
The third stage is in the coion; drying, dominated by the **pungent taste**.

24. POST-DIGESTION, *VIPAK*

The final outcome of digestion is absorption and elimination.
The six tastes are reduced to three in their post-digestive effect,
known as *vipaka*.

Sweet and salty tastes   have a sweet *vipaka;*
Sour   has a sour *vipaka;*
Bitter, astringent & pungent   have a pungent *vipaka*

Herbs, particularly over long-term use, tend to aggravate the
dosha of which *vipaka* they possess.
* Sweet and salty substances promote salivary and other
  Kaphic secretions.
* Sour herbs promote stomach acid, bile and other manifesta
  tions of *Pitta*.
* Bitter, pungent and astringent herbs increase dryness and
  gas in the colon, thus aggravating *Vata*.

Sweet and sour *vipakas*, owing to their moistening property,
allow for easy and comfortable discharge of urine, faeces and
intestinal gas. They aggravate *Kapha*, while they alleviate *Vata*.

Sour *vipaka* aggravates *Pitta* while sweet *vipakas* alleviate it.

Pungent *vipaka*, by its drying property, creates difficulty and
discomfort in the discharge of waste products, tending to
cause gas, constipation and painful urination. Pungent *vipaka*
tends to aggravate *Vata* and *Pitta* over a period of time.

25. SPECIAL POTENCY, *PRABHAVA*

Possessing more subtle and specific qualities that transcend thought and cannot be placed into a system of energetics, is the 'special potency', *prabhava*, of a herb.

It is its special pre-disposition, uniqueness, apart from any general rules about it. This also includes the occult properties of the plant, auric action, astral effect, magnetic effect, radiation and its capacity to affect the mind and psyche on a direct and subtle level, transcending thought and the reasoning of the materialistic mind.

26. CREATING BALANCE THROUGH PROPER DIET

Diet in Ayurveda is tailored according to individual needs, based on a person's mind-body type and the imbalances that may be present in one's physiology.

It is best to follow a diet that pacifies your main dosha. A *vata*-pacifying diet, for example, includes food that tends to have an influence on decreasing *vata*.

The following table will assist.

26.1 How tastes affect the Doshas:

Decrease Vata :	Sweet, Sour, Salty
Increase Vata:	Pungent, Bitter, Astringent
Decrease Pitta:	Sweet, Bitter, Astringent
Increase Pitta:	Pungent, Sour, Salty
Decrease Kapha:	Pungent, Bitter, Astringent
Increase Kapha:	Sweet, Sour, Salty

The use of vegetables, fruit, herbs and spices is known as *Ayurvedic Botanical Medicine*.

To find out what body type (*dosha*) you are, a self assessment Chart can be found at the back of this book.

27. AWARENESS AND CHOICE

We are what we eat is the old adage. Choose well. Food can be a conscious choice.

It is good to follow your likes and dislikes for tastes etc., but you should consider the fact that your desires may be the result of bad habits which cause an imbalance in your physiology.

Eat when you're hungry. If you are really hungry, do you bother to go and find a nice table with beautiful dishes to eat your food on? No, the moment you see a mandarin, you peel it and eat it, even while you're walking. You might not even want to peel it! But if you take the mandarin and ask: Who produced it? Who planted it? Where did it come from? Is it properly certified? You are not really hungry!

- Avoid eating before the previous meal has fully digested (approx. 3-6 hrs between meals). This does not apply to Pitta.

- Use your hunger like a fuel gauge : 0 is so empty that you are starving, 10 is so full you can barely move.

- Eat when your appetite is at 2 or 3, i.e. when you are really hungry, but will survive if you have to wait an hour. Stop at about 7, when you could eat more but you are comfortably full.

- Do not eat too slowly or too quickly.
  Eat up to $^3/_4$ of your capacity. Leaving some space in the stomach (about $^1/_3$ to $^1/_4$ empty) makes digestion a lot easier. At the end of your meal you should not feel hungry or too full.

- Always sit down to eat and eat roughly at the same time each day.

- Eat in a calm and settled atmosphere with pleasant company, environment and a settled mind.

- Eat at a moderate pace and don't talk when chewing your food.

- If possible, make lunch the main meal of the day.

- Breakfast and dinner should be light in quantity and quality.

- Avoid working, reading or watching TV during meals. Attention is what activates everything in this universe. You digest the environment through all of your senses and will metabolize all those stress and fear chemicals into your body if you watch a violent TV show while eating.

- Never eat when you are upset. It is better to process emotional upsets in other ways than using food to feed an emotional need.

- Choose food free of chemicals and other poisons and of superior nutritional value, flavour and quality.

- Eat freshly cooked meals and foods that are fresh, alive and not over cooked. Avoid eating stale left-overs. Prepare enough for one meal and finish it. The more prana you take in, the more vital energy is available to you.

- Include all six tastes (sweet, sour, salty, pungent, bitter, astringent) in each meal, with consideration to your constitution. This will ensure that the meal is nutritionally balanced and you will feel satisfied after eating it.

- Chew all food well. The digestive process begins in the mouth.

Blood is composed out of the same ocean where we have come from. Salt is the catalyst of our actions. Our thoughts move like waves through our salt-sea blood, creating the foam of our intelligence. Food is made delicious with salt. Should we exaggerate it by a grain, the taste becomes too strong. A strawberry with a grain of salt is sweeter than a raw strawberry. A second grain, though makes it taste like vinegar!

By eating fruits and sweets we expand the mind, inhibiting the ability to concentrate. Salt is the balance for this expansion. It contracts the mind to the limits of our potential understanding. Salt is the natural and psychological judge of our spiritual actions. We cannot think more than the salt in our blood permits us to think. Sodium and potassium in our cells determine the contraction and expansion of our imagination.

The greater our activity, the greater our intake of salt should be. Before discovering fire and salt, human beings were slow paced. Yet activity is the sacred movement that creates human beings. From the greatest activity of the heavens, we were made. Through activity we grow into infinite dimensions. When we work, the oxygen combines with the sodium in our cells, creating potassium. The more salt we take, the more active we should be; then the more oxygen we breathe and the more potassium we produce.

Since the advent of computers and other slave-machines in our lives, we have become so inactive. Remaining inactive, we

84

inhale less oxygen, upsetting the sodium-potassium balance and making the maintenance of a normal metabolism extremely difficult. Sedentary office workers need less salt, as do bedridden sick people.

Food and herbs when taken, digested and assimilated in the body increase the similar qualities and elements of the body. On the other hand, substances with opposite properties antagonise the increased elements in the body and maintain a balanced state.

- Reduce raw foods. Ayurveda suggests not taking large amounts of raw foods. Organic, well-ripened fruits are okay.

- Overcooking destroys vitamins and other essential nutri ents, but properly cooked food tastes and smells better and is easier to digest.

- Milk should not be taken with meals that include mixed tastes ie. (vegetable/lentil combinations) but can be taken with toast, cereals or sweet-tasting foods and separate from a meal.

- Eggs, sour fruits, yoghurt, radish, garlic or salt, are particularly incompatible with milk.

- Honey should not be heated by cooking or by adding to hot drinks.

- Do not take Yoghurt and cheese at night.

- Do not eat just before bedtime. A glass of warm milk is good if hungry and will help you sleep.

Thirst dictates the need to sip water or other beverages during meals. These should not be below room temperature or they will dull your appetite. It is preferable to avoid large amounts of liquids before and after meals.

Reduce ice-cold food and beverages as they upset the digestive process. Taste buds and digestive juices work best at body temperature. The food and beverages many people tend to take ice cold don't taste that good at body temperature, so they try to sneak them past their taste buds by first numbing them with ice.

Sit quietly for a few minutes after meals and then take a short, calm walk (100 steps).

28. STOCKING THE KITCHEN

In the very beginning, the Lord said in the Garden of Eden unto Adam, the first man: *'Behold I have given you every herb bearing seed, which is upon the face of all the earth, and every tree, on which is the fruit yielding seed; to you it shall be for meat.'*

Genesis. 1.29

Nature has been bountiful in presenting us food full of beautiful natural seasonings to enjoy the true taste of her fine foods.

A powerful tool for maintaining the dynamic balance of health is the wise use of botanical medicine, herbs and spices. Nature has provided healing solutions in the form of medicinal plants and foods to balance unhealthy lifestyles, seasonal changes and other doshic imbalances. These herbs and spices were not common in traditional Western kitchens but are increasingly available from specialist Chinese and Indian grocers, delicatessens, health food shops, and even supermarkets.

Sadly, many of us are accustomed to diets that are rich in artificial seasonings, chemicals, salts and sugars.

Creative sauce making uses the gifts of natural oils, seeds, herbs and spices for delicious taste as well as for cleansing and healing.

Following is a glossary that includes the 'natural pharmacies' within the kitchen and specialities that make for the taste in life. It is sectioned into:

1	Nuts & Seeds	5	Oils
2	Fruits & Vegetables	6	Dairy
3	Herbs & Spices	7	Water
4	Grains, Pulses & Beans		

29. NATURAL PHARMACY WITHIN THE KITCHEN:

29.1 NUTS & SEEDS

*'Out of the ground God planted every tree
that is pleasant to the sight and good for food.'*
Genesis.

Almonds *Badam*
Sweet tasting nut, producing a heating energy. Improves hair health & shine. Phytochemicals found to suppress lung and prostate tumor cell growth. Helps lower cholesterol. Increases Kapha and Pitta, decreases Vata.

Cashews *Kaju*
Rich in zinc, a mineral being researched as a cure for the common cold.

Hazelnuts
Like almonds and pecans, helpful in lowering cholesterol.

Pecan nuts
Lower blood cholesterol, effective in fighting heart disease.

Poppy seeds *Khus khus*
The minute, kidney-shaped, bluish-black seeds have a pleasant nutty taste and crunchy texture, used in Middle Eastern and European cuisine as topping for breads and cakes, or ground up and sweetened as a pastry filling.

White poppy seeds are much used in Indian cuisine, especially as a thickener for sauces and gravies (flours are generally not used in Indian cuisines for this purpose). They are even smaller than black poppy seeds, have a similar flavour and are a creamy-white. Don't substitute them for black poppy seeds in baking, as they impart a bitter flavour to the dish. Pungent, astringent, sweet, they are heating in energy. Decreases Vata and Kapha, increases Pitta.

Sesame *Til*
Seeds - Rich in calcium & thiamine. Good for bones and teeth.

Sunflower *Surajmukhi*
Seeds - Related to mood stability. Improves health and shine of hair, reduces chance of dry scalp, lacklustre strands and split ends.

Walnuts *Akhrot*
Thiamine, Vitamin B6, Folic acid, Phospholipid fatty acid, Linoleic acid. Good for the brain. Reduces risk of stroke.

29.2   FRUIT & VEGETABLES

Apples *Sev*
Good for strengthening the body.

Asparagus *Satavar, Satavari*
Sweet tasting vegetable, produces cooling. Diuretic, laxative,
tonic. Decreases Pitta and Kapha.

Avocadoes *Makhajan Phal*
Earthy. Go with everything. Good mixers.

Bananas *Kela*
Mellow. Sweet, laxative. Unripe, constipative.

Beetroot *Chukandar*
Beet sugars help cultivate friendly bacteria in the intestines
and fight cholesterol.

Bhajjiyas, Pakoras, Onion/Vegetable fritter
Delicious raw onion fritters in lentil batter. Many other vegetables can be frittered in the same batter.

Bitter Gourd *Karela*
A vegetable with a characteristic bitter taste. Modern science
has ascertained that the bitter gourd is particularly high in
vitamin C. Favoured as an appetite tonic, traditionally used by
Ayurvedic doctors to treat anorexia, as a stimulant for sluggish
livers and to dissolve kidney stones resulting from dehydra-
tion during the hot Indian summer. In the pharmacology of
Ayurveda, the gourd is renowned for its capacity to lower
exaggerated sexual drive and is also efficacious against intestinal worms, which probably explains why Indian mothers force
bitter gourd down their children's throats as ruthlessly as
Western mothers insist that their children eat spinach.

Blueberries *Ber*
Reverse loss of balance and coordination; improve short-term memory, protect urinary tract against infections.

Brinjal *Baingan*
see Eggplant

Carrot *Gajar*
Boosts immume system functions. Helps solve skin disorders. Vitamin A or retinoic acid, found in carrots may block cancer in the body by making cancer cells self-destruct .

Celery
Anti-inflammatory. Traditionally used as an arthritis treatment.

Cherries *Cheri*
Brain and nerve food. Good fór thinking. antioxidant; anti-inflammatory - relieve the pain of gout and arthritis.

Coconut *Narial, nariyal*
Sweet, cooling coastal tropical fruit, high in proteins, minerals and vitamins and representing an ecosystem complete in itself, the coconut provides milk, water, cream, oil and hard flesh. Fresh green coconuts are cooling. Acts as a refrigerant, diuretic, tonic. Eat dried coconut sparingly. Rich. Strain out pulp. May be substituted for yoghurt or almonds in recipes. Decreases Pitta and Vata, increases Kapha.

Dates *Khajoor*
Have been found to reverse the progression of prostate cancer.

Eggplant, *Baingan*
The fruit of this plant varies in shape from large and spherical to elongated and berry-like and it is either purple or white in colour. Clinical tests have shown that the eggplant is anti-

carcinogenic, anti-convulsant and valuable in reducing cholesterol. The alkaline properties of the fruit can occasion allergies
but those properties are considerably diminished by marinat-
ing or roasting them.
To describe three popular methods:
1. Coat in turmeric, then deep-fry in mustard oil
2. Coat in salt, saute, then simmer in yoghurt
3. Roast over a flame, then mash with chopped ginger, green
   chillies and fresh coriander leaves ... yum.

Figs *Anjir*
Promote strong, healthy bones. Contains 3.2 times more
calcium than other fruits.

Gooseberry *Amalaki*
Reduces acidity. Cooling effect. Good for eyes, memory.
Chew after meal.

Grapes *Anguor*
Invite divine love. Cleansing mental food.

Green chillies *Hari mirchi*
Unripe pods of various chilli peppers. They impart a delicious
flavour as well as heat.

Kelp
Salty, sweet sea-weed, heating in energy, with a sweet post-
digestive effect. Decreases Vata, increases Kapha and Pitta.

Lemon *Nimbu*
Sour fruit with cooling energy and a pungent post-digestive
effect. Decreases Pitta and Vata.

Mangoes *Aam*
Delicious heavenly fruit. The mango tree fruits in the hot

summer months of India, that precede the monsoon rains. As mangoes are highly effective against sunstroke, a variety of summer drinks are made from pulped mangoes to lower body temperature and assuage thirst during this season. Strained with black salt, molasses and cumin, mango juice becomes Panna. Mixed with milk, the juice is turned into Mango-Fool. The pulp is also used in decoctions for the treatment of diabetes and blood pressure problems.

Traditionally, ripe mangoes are kept in buckets of cold water. This ensures that the fruit remains fresh and it also eliminates the turpentine resin in the stalk. Strongly scented, with a slightly astringent taste in their sweetness, mangoes are rich in vitamin C. They are used in an Indian diet throughout the year. In summer when the body is losing salt through perspiration, raw mangoes are sliced and eaten with salt, or they are pickled in oil and kept for the winter months as a useful antidote for colds. Perfectly balanced. Heating.

Melons *Kharbooja*
Purifiers of body and spirit.

Onion *Pyaz*
With a few exceptions, no Indian dish is complete without onion. The finer the onions are chopped, the better the flavour and texture of the dish. Pungent, sweet, heating vegetable, with sweet post-digestive effect, it is often regarded as an aphrodisiac. Decreases Vata and Kapha, increases Pitta.

Oranges *Santra*
Expanding. Exhuberant.

Papayas *Papiya*
Digestion of food.

Peaches *Aadu*
Sweet and temporary.

Plums *AluBukara*
Energise the intestines; heighten the spirit.

Pineapples *Annanas*
Emotional strength, self confidence.

Raisins *Kishmish*
Protect the heart; help sustain normal blood sugar levels; acid slows down the development of colon cancer.

Spinach *Palak*
Green garden vegetable with succulent leaves.

Tomatoes *Tamatar*
Blood purifiers.

Turnip *Shalgam*
Fleshy, globular white root used as a vegetable.

Watermelon *Tarbooj*
Water fruit, in tune with the moon and good for the kidneys. Balancing.

29.3 HERBS AND SPICES

Ajwan celery seeds
Tiny, light-brown spice seeds closely related to caraway and cummin with a very strong thyme and oregano flavour. They aid digestion and are used to relieve stomach problems. Pungent in taste and post-digestive effect; energy is heating. Stimulant, diaphoretic, antispasmodic. Decreases Kapha and Vata, increases Pitta.

Alfalfa
Astringent, sweet grass of cooling energy with pungent post-digestive effects. Diuretic, antipyretic. Decreases Pitta and Kapha, increases Vata.

Allspice *kabab cheene*
Allspice is not a combination of different spices but is produced from the dried berries of the Jamaican pimento, which has a flavour similar to that of cardamom, cinnamon and nutmeg. It is not a traditional ingredient in Indian cooking but has come to be used in many pilau, biriani and Mughlai dishes.

Aloe Vera *ghee kanvar; kumari*
Bitter, astringent, pungent, sweet juice of cactus plant, produces cooling energy and can be used as a bitter tonic, rejuvenative and purgative. It is tri-doshic and so can be used for all three *doshas*.

Asafoetida *hing*
Digestive and flavouring. Helps in oil and fat digestion. Aromatic resin from the root of the giant fennel. In spring, when the plant is about to bloom, the stems and roots are cut. Milky resin exudes from the cut surfaces and is scraped off. More exudes as successive slices of root are removed over a period

of three months. The gummy resin is sun-dried into a solid mass that is then sold in solid wax-like pieces, or more conveniently in powdered form. Due to the presence of sulphur compounds, asafoetida has a distinctive pungent flavour reminiscent of shallots or garlic. Used in minute quantities it adds a delicious flavour and is an integral part of the strict vegetarian diet of the Brahmins. It is never used in recipes for meat or poultry. Favour the mild yellow asafoetida and not the grey variety. Pungent in taste, heating in energy. Decreases Vata and Kapha, increases Pitta.

Basil *Tulsi (Tulsi* : holy basil)
Modern science has established that this modest aromatic shrub perceptibly purifies the air within a wide radius of its vicinity, proving most effective just before sunrise, the time when it is ritually circled by the devout. Medically the plant provides a pharmacopoeia for the entire household. Its leaves are crushed in honey and used to treat coughs, colds, bronchitis and to reduce fevers. An infusion of basil leaves and ginger is India's most popular remedy for stomach ache in children. Its essential oil is an antiseptic and insect repellent, while its root, reduced to a paste, soothes bites and stings, acting even as an antidote to snake venom and scorpion bites!

Bay leaves *tejpatta*
The laurel wreaths which were worn by the ancient Roman Emperors were made of bay leaves. The highly aromatic leaves of the laurel tree, thick, dark green and glossy on their upper surface used fresh or dried, have a slightly bitter, pungent flavour. Heating, carminative, stimulant, expectorant. Decreases Vata and Kapha, increases Pitta.

Black pepper *kali mirch*
See Pepper.

Caraway seeds *shahjeera, kala jeera*
Closely related to cumin, but has a milder flavour which does
not dominate.

Cardamom *elaichi*
Cooling effect. Sweet in taste. Digestive. Flavouring. Mouth
freshner.

Prized by foreigners for their fragrant aroma and delicate
taste, cardamom seeds were called 'Grains of Paradise.' A
perennial of the ginger family, cardamom grows in the moist
tropical regions of Southern India and Sri Lanka and is the
world's third most costly spice, topped only by saffron and
vanilla.

There are two varieties: Large black pods, *Badi elaichi*, used in
certain curries, pilaus and biryanis and the inner seeds often
used for making garam masala. The small green pods referred
to as *choti elaichi* are used in most curries, pilaus and some
sweet dishes. The odour and flavour is reminiscent of lemon-
rind and eucalyptus, it is used in rice dishes, milk sweets and
halva. It is also chewed as a breath freshener and digestive aid
after a meal.

When the recipe calls for whole cardamom, open up the pods
slightly to extract the full flavour, which is in the seeds. Best
to grind small quantities at home, using a coffee mill, because
it loses its natural oil quickly and also loses its flavour. Has a
pungent, sweet taste, produces heating energy and a pungent
post digestive effect. Decreases Vata and Kapha, increases
Pitta. Stimulant, carminative, expectorant.

Cayenne
see Pepper, *kalimrich*

Carob
Rich non-meat calcium source. An astringent herb, especially helpful in treating diarrhoea in children. Used as a substitute for chocolate.

Chillies *mirch*
Fresh chillies are nutritious, being rich in vitamins A and C. They also stimulate sluggish digestion. The seeds are the hottest part and you can tame the heat of the chilli by removing the seeds.

Be warned, the smoke given off by frying chillis is very pungent and will cause your eyes to sting and bring on a coughing fit if you get too full a breath of it. Keep your nose well away from the pot.

Dried chillies are the dried pods of the capsicum plant, vary in size and heat and can be obtained whole or crushed. When chillis are ripe they are usually a rich red colour. These are then dried in the sun to give us the dried red, *Lal Mirchi*, which are very different in flavour from fresh green or fresh ripe chillis. Tiny chillies are generally very hot - use sparingly.

• Chervil

• Chives

Cinnamon *dalchini*
A moderate-sized, bushy evergreen tree of the laurel family, native to India and Sri Lanka, the thin inner bark sheaths are sun-dried and packed one inside the other to produce 'sticks' or 'quills'.. True cinnamom has a more delicate flavour than Cassia tree-bark cinnamon.

Cinnamon is an essential ingredient in garam masala. It is

often used whole in curries, pilaus and biryanis and is brewed with cloves and aniseed as a medicinal drink to fight the symptoms of colds, coughs and flu. It acts as a stimulant, imparts a pungent, sweet, astringent taste, heating energy and sweet post-digestive effect. Store in air-tight container. Decreases Vata and Kapha, increases Pitta.

Clove *long, lavang*
The fragrant clove, highly antiseptic, today so mundanely associated with the clove oil used as a remedy for toothaches, is one of the spices over which the nations of Europe went to war during the sixteenth and seventeenth centuries.

Nail-shaped pink buds from neat evergreens, which when hand picked and dried in the sun, turn reddish brown to become the cloves with which we are familiar. Good cloves have a strong, pungent aroma and flavour and should be well-formed, plump and oily. Cloves are an essential ingredient in garam masala. Use in measured quantities. The flavour overpowers. Always buy whole. Ground cloves do not contain the essential oil that flavours a dish.

Heating, stimulant, carminative, aphrodisiac, expectorant. Decreases Vata, Kapha, and increases Pitta.

Coconut, dessicated *Kopra powder*
Convenient alternative to the rather time-consuming process of preparing fresh coconut for use in a recipe.

Coffee
Coffee contains caffeine which is a very powerful stimulant and is on the list of banned drugs drawn up by the International Olympic Committee. Many experts believe that if coffee was only discovered in the 1990's it would be sold through pharmacies or by prescription only. A cup of strong instant

coffee contains 90 milligrams of caffeine, a cappuccino 105 milligrams, a cup of strong Tea 50 milligrams, a can of CocaCola 50 milligrams, a dark chocolate bar 33 milligrams and a No-Doz tablet 100 milligrams of caffeine.
Next time you have insomnia or a headache, have a look at your caffeine intake for the day.

Coriander *dhaniya*
Hara Dhania, bunches of fresh fan-like lower leaves, and feathery upper ones from a hardy annual plant, coriander is one of the most commonly used flavouring herbs in the world for its unique warm-bodied taste and smell and as a very beautiful garnish. The tender stalks have the same flavour as that of the leaves - chop finely and use along with the leaves.

Coriander is easy to grow in any type of soil and can therefore be grown in a window box throughout winter and in the garden in summer.

It is the single most important spice in Indian cooking. Its mild and slightly sweet flavour blends well with almost all Indian dishes and it controls their basic flavour.

Coriander seeds are almost round, brown to yellowish-red, with a warm, distinctive fragrance and a pleasant taste -mild and sweet yet slightly pungent, reminiscent of a combination of sage and lemon. Gently roast before grinding to bring out its full flavour. The plant is particularly effective as a diuretic (to increase the flow of urine) and as a refrigerant to break fevers. The crushed and roasted seeds mixed with warm water are used as a gargle in cases of thrush of the mouth, in a barley poultice for ulcers, or mixed with cold water as an eye lotion in cases of conjunctivitis. As a medicine coriander was employed by Hippocrates and other Greek physicians, so that its medicinal values were already known by the time the

Romans introduced coriander to Europe; explaining its presence in the very early European medical herbaria. It's bitter, pungent taste produces cooling energy, with pungent post-digestive effects. It is tri-doshic. Digestive. Appetiser.

Cummin *jeera*
Pungent aromatic spice. Helps to digest starch and cellulose (green vegetables). Use in *sabji* (various vegetables).

Two varieties: black cumin, *kala jeera* and white cumin, *safed jeera*. Although both are widely used, one cannot be substituted for the other as they each have their own quite distinctive flavour.

Seeds of the small annual herb of the parsley family are yellowish-brown, similar in appearance to the caraway seed, but taste quite different, are longer and have a pungent, strongly aromatic and slightly bitter flavour. Like most spice-seeds, flavour and aroma emerge best after they have been dry roasted or added to hot oil and the great virtue of the cumin-seed lies in its digestive properties when roasted. It is easily digested and very effective in expelling gas from the stomach and intestines. Producing cooling energy, pungent post-digestive effect. It is tri-doshic.

Curry leaves *curry patta, mitha neem*
Thin, shiny, dark-green leaves are highly aromatic when fresh. Dried leaves are inferior but sometimes this is all that is available.

Curry powder, Mixed spices
'Invented' by a British Army officer for the non-Indian market, notably Britain, who made a fortune from it. See Garam Masala which is more ethnic than curry powder.

• Dill

Fennel *saof, saunf*
Finely divided feathery green foliage and golden-yellow flowers, used both as a herb and for its aromatic seed.

The oval, greenish, or yellowish-brown seeds resemble tiny watermelons. They emit an agreeable, sweet, pungent fragrance similar to that of anise. Used commonly as an after-dinner digestive, they are dry-roasted and chewed, freshening the breath with a cooling energy, stimulating digestion and producing a sweet post-digestive effect. They are tri-doshic.

Fenugreek *methi*
The seeds are small, hard, yellowish-brown, smooth and oblong, with a little groove across one corner. They have a slightly bitter, pungent, sweet taste, reminiscent of burnt sugar and maple and need to be lightly dry-roasted or fried to extract their characteristic flavour. Over-roasting or over-frying results in excessive bitter flavours. Producing heating energy, pungent post-digestive effects. Reduces Vata and Kapha, and increases Pitta.

Early home-grown, fresh, young fenugreek leaves which are very much like watercress, are also popular, used in salads, breads, vegetable dishes and savouries. They cannot be substituted for the seeds.

Flax seed *javas*
Contains many nutritional components, including fibre and ligands which inhibit cancers, such as breast cancer; Alpha-linoleic acid, which helps ward off heart attacks; helps inhibit auto-immune diseases like rheumatoid arthritis, severe menstrual cramps and perhaps even depression. Also contains omega-4 fattty acids found in some meats.

Garam Masala

'Hot mixture' - A blend of dry-roasted and ground spices used to warm the body, the main ingredients being cardamom, cinnamon and cloves - which govern the taste of the mixture and commonly include dried chillies, black pepper, coriander and cumin. Other spices such as ajwan, mace, nutmeg, fennel, bay leaves, ginger, white and green pepper, as well as other ingredients, such as sesame seeds, coconut and saffron are also used according to the region and geographical location.

Garlic *lasan, rasona*

Contemporary clinical tests have confirmed that garlic destroys bacteria. The compound allicin, an antibiotic which has such a broad spectrum as an effective agent against disease-spreading microbes is destroyed by cooking, so garlic then loses its antibiotic power. Indians eat garlic raw with oil and chillies, as chutney, or with salt as a blood cleanser and for nervous disorders such as headaches and hysteria. Fresh garlic is a vital ingredient in Indian cooking. Powdered garlic or garlic salt cannot be substituted as the flavour is so very different. Some very puritanical sects fear its reputation as an aphrodisiac, or very strict vegetarians who believe that in uprooting a garlic bulb from the ground they may accidentally kill an insect, don't eat garlic.

From its very inception, Ayurveda has used garlic to treat a wide range of diseases: rheumatism; for the lungs as an expectorant and powerful decongestant; for the heart to lower blood pressure and reduce high cholesterol; for the stomach, as an anthelmintic that expels round worms from the system; for gynaecological problems, to regulate or bring on menstruation and for improving libido. Garlic is heating in energy, with a pungent post-digestive effect. It has all the tastes (sweet, salty, pungent, bitter, astringent) except sour. Decreases Vata and Kapha, increases Pitta.

Tested in the modern laboratory, garlic has found to be anti-protozoan, anti-parasitic and anti-viral, as well as an antibiotic and antifungal in cases of tuberculosis and meningitis. But perhaps the most important use of this humble bulb, which Ayurveda calls 'the wonder food', will be discovered when its properties in boosting the natural immune system of the human body are fully understood.

Ginger *adarak*
'The universal remedy', dried ginger is called the 'great medicament' against colds, coughs, rhinitis, bronchitis and indigestion. It is a prostaglandin inhibitor, similar to Asprin and other nonsteroidal anti-inflammatories that are general prescription anti-arthritic drugs. Ginger is prescribed for abdominal distension, colic, diarrhoea and nausea. Contemporary medicine considers ginger as a potent antidote to motion sickness as well as being anti-cholesterol and an anticoagulant. However, Ayurvedic medicine notes that people suffering from hyperacidity and gastric ulcers should avoid ginger.

The thick, white, tuberous underground stems, or rhizomes, which thrive in the tropical areas of the world have a spicy-sweet aroma and a hot, clean taste. Young 'green' ginger is especially appreciated for its fibre-free texture and mild flavour. It can be minced, sliced, pureed, shredded or cut into fine julienne strips. Ginger powder, or ginger preserved in vinegar, is not a substitute for fresh ginger, having lost its volatile essential oil and being sometimes stale or adulterated. Heating energy, sweet post-digestive taste. Decreases Vata, Kapha, increases Pitta.

Honey *shahad*
Sweet, pungent, astringent in taste, heating in energy, with a sweet post-digestive effect. Decreases Vata and Kapha, increases Pitta. **Sugar** however, is sweet in taste but cooling in

energy.

Kewra - essence, *kevada*
Essential flavouring derived from the pandanus palm, growing in the humid, swampy backwater areas of Southern India and South-East Asia. The flowers have an exquisite rose-like perfume.

Lavender
Pungent taste, cooling energy, sweet post-digestive effect. Decreases Pitta and Kapha.

• Lemon peel

Mango powder *amchoor*
A tan coloured powder made from grinding small sun-dried green mangoes, gives a slightly sour, pungent taste.

• Marjoram

Mint *pudina*
Having a fresh, strong, sweet, tangy flavour, with a cool after taste, mint is best used fresh rather than dried. There are many species of mint and classification is not easy because they cross - hybridise easily. Spearmint and peppermint are the two most common mints, the round-leaved varieties of apple mint, Bowles mint and pineapple mint are the best mints for cooking. Spearmint, decreases Kapha and Pitta.

Mustard *rai* or *sarson*
Black, brown, yellow are among the many varieties of mustard.

Brown mustard seeds, *rai*, are fried in hot oil or ghee to extract their nutty, pungent flavour before being added to soups, chutneys or vegetable dishes in Indian cooking. Heating in energy. Decreases Kapha and Vata, increases Pitta.

Yellow mustard seeds are less pungent than the darker varieties and are strongly preservative, discouraging moulds and bacteria, hence their inclusion in pickles commonly used in European cuisine.

Pounded mustard seeds form the base of the immense varieties of commercial brand condiment known as mustard, made from different combinations of hulled and unhulled yellow or brown seeds. Pungency of mustard is due to an essential oil which is not present in the seed or powder, but forms when the crushed seed is mixed with water. An enzyme then causes a bitter substance in the seed to react with the water and the hot taste of mustard emerges.

Nutmeg *jaiphal*
Nutmeg and mace come from the same tree, mace being the outer part of the fruit and nutmeg the kernel, or seed. The fragrant nut found in the centre of the fleshy apricot-resembling fruit, of the densely foliated evergreen tree, *Myristica fragrans*. When the fruit is ripe it splits in half, revealing the beautiful, brilliant scarlet, net-like membrane, or avil, known as mace, which closely enwraps a brittle shell containing the glossy brown, oily nutmeg.

Nutmeg is egg-shaped and about 2.5 cm (1 inch) in diameter, with a pungent and highly spiced flavour, heating in energy, with a sedative action. Decreases Vata and Kapha, increases Pitta.

Whole nutmeg is best ground straight into the dish into which it is being used, as once grated, nutmeg quickly loses its flavour.

Onion seeds *kalonji*
From the Nigella plant. Seeds are used whole for flavouring vegetables and in pickles.

•Oregano

Paprika sweet chilli powder
Brilliant red powder made from the dried, sweet, chilli-pepper pods. It is not hot and can be used in generous quantities, giving dishes a rich red hue - its primary use. It is also very nutritious, having a high vitamin C content, heating. Decreases Kapha and Vata, increases Pitta.

Parsley
Healthful parsley leaves with their familiar mild, agreeable flavour, are an excellent source of vitamin C, iron, iodine, and other minerals. Parsley is appealing to the eye, nose and tastebuds, will sweeten the breath and is a natural herbal deodoriser. It is one of the best known and most extensively used culinary herbs in western cuisine. Heating energy, pungent post-digestive effect. Decreases Kapha and Vata, increases Pitta.

Pepper *kali mrich*
Black, white and green pepper are all obtained from the same berries at different stages of maturity.

White pepper is produced from fully ripened berries, which are greenish-yellow when picked and at the point of turning red. They are then soaked in water and the outer hull is rubbed off. The grey inner berries are sun-dried until they turn creamy white, to become what is known as milder flavoured white pepper.

Green peppercorns are soft, immature berries that have been picked and preserved in brine, or freeze dried.

Berries picked whilst green, left in heaps to ferment, sun-dried and allowed to shrivel and turn dark brown or black ... thus the whole berry, including the dark outer hull forms what is known as black pepper, characterised by a penetrating odour and a hot, biting and extremely pungent flavour. A single black pepper corn is often added to tea as an aromatic for the throat and as a stimulant, or a couple of peppers are sucked as throat lozenges. Ayurvedic medicine considers black pepper harmless to the stomach and administers it for the alleviation of colds, coughs, catarrh and bronchial complaints; as well as purges for worms and in preparations for constipation. Heating in energy. Black pepper decreases Kapha and Vata, increases Pitta. Stimulant, expectorant, carminative. Hot. Appetizer. Improves circulatory function. Cleans lymphatic system.

Rose water *Gulab jal*
The diluted essence of rose petals is used as a flavouring agent, especially in *lassi*, the refreshing, icy-cold sweet-yoghurt based beverage and in milk balls in rose syrup, *gulab jamun* and *rasgoolas*.

Saffron *Kesar*
The world's most expensive spice, the brilliant stigmas are hand-picked daily, just as the plant opens in the early morning. Between 75,000 and 250,000 stigmas are required to produce just one pound of saffron. After picking, the saffron is dried in sieves over low heat, then stored immediately. The final product is a compressed, highly aromatic matted mass of narrow, thread-like, dark-orange to reddish-brown strands, about 2.5 cm (1-inch) long.

Saffron has a pleasantly spicy, pungent, slightly bitter honey-like taste with a potent colouring power. Be sure to purchase the real thing - saffron is often adulterated. The strands should be soaked and ground or slightly dry-roasted and powdered before using. A big pinch of saffron is sufficient to colour a whole dish.

Salt *namak*
Black salt, *kala namak*, is a reddish-grey variety of salt with a distinct 'hard-boiled egg' flavour. It is also known as Himalayan black salt, as it comes from the Himalayas and originates from when the oceans covered the earth.
Celtic salt. Greyish salt, doesn't have drying agents or other chemicals etc. to make it flow well.
Both celtic salt and black salt are superior products, and have 87 different minerals in them.
Sea salt is not the conditioned, sparkling salt usually sold in grocery stores. It comes from the ocean, while the other comes from the laboratories and factories. A grey, unwashed kind and a lighter one which has previously been washed in sea water. Both of these contain many natural mineral salts. Some cerealians roast their salt before using it to liberate excess chlorine gas.
Vegetable salt is a mixture of sea salt and vegetable seasoning like onion, celery, parsley, paprika, garlic, horseradish powder and sage.

Sumac
Seeds ground to a purple-red powder and used to add a sour, pleasantly astringent taste to recipes as a preferred substitute for lemon. The extracted juice of the soaked seeds is used in salads and in some vegetable dishes to impart a tamarind-like flavour. Sumac has a pleasant, rounded, fruity sourness which is well worth experimenting with.

Tamarind *imli*

The fresh pulp extracted from the brown pods of the tamarind tree has a sour fruity taste. Although tamarind has been used against scurvy in India since the most remote times, it is also known for its effectiveness against mouth and throat infections. Indeed, the most famous tamarind tree in India stands over the tomb of the legendary Indian singer, Tansen, whose golden voice led the Great Moghul, the Emperor Akbar, to name Tansen one of the nine gems of his court. Four centuries later, India's finest classical singers still travel to Tansen's tomb to pluck leaves from this tamarind tree to make into throat gargles, in the hope that their voices will become as pure as their legendary predecessor's.

Tamarind is available in different forms commercially. The crudest consists of blocks of partly dried, unpitted, broken, stocky, fibrous pods. They should be macerated in water to extract the sour brown tamarind juice, as should another form which comes in blocks of fibrous pulp without seeds. The most convenient is tamarind concentrate, which can be used straight from the jar.

Valued as an antidote to heat stroke, tamarind sherbet lowers body temperature. It makes excellent sweet-and-sour chutneys and sauces and is used in vegetable dishes and curries. Sour and sweet in taste, heating in energy. Stimulant, carminative, laxative. Decreases Vata and Kapha, increases Pitta.

Turmeric *haldi*

The short, waxy, orange-yellow rhizomes (underground stems) are boiled, cleaned, sun-dried and then ground to a fine, aromatic yellowish powder that is used as an essential ingredient in Indian cooking. Turmeric introduces colour - brilliant yellow ...watch out, it's colour stains most things! and imparts a slightly bitter, pungent warmth to a dish. Overuse produces excessive colour and bitterness. Turmeric powder has been found to significantly increase the mucous content in gastric disorders. Heating in energy, with pungent post-digestive effects, it is a stimulant, antibacterial, vulnerary. Decreases Kapha and Vata.

Vanilla

Flavouring obtained from the dried, cured, partially ripe pods. Whole vanilla beans are cooked with creams, custards and sauces. They can be washed, dried and re-used. The white crystalline compound called vanillin, present only in cured black pods provides the delicately sweet, spicy and persistent aroma that characterises the fragrant principle of vanilla.

29.4 PULSES, LEGUMES, BEANS, PEAS & GRAINS

Rich in essential iron, Vitamin B, complex carbohydrates and amino acids (protein) they can be delicious and there are so many ways to use them.

Pulses (peas, beans and lentils) are the most potent and more easily assimilated when sprouted. Within the bean is the potential for a whole tree, perhaps this is why they are called *the pulse of life*. For many vegetarians they are, in some form or another, a constant feature of vegetarian meals.

India has the largest vegetarian community in the world and the vegetarian cuisine from traditional Indian recipies is delicious and nutritious. (Western society has recently recognised the health-giving properties of vegetarian meals and is changing towards vegetarian eating). In Indian cuisine **dried beans** are, for the most part made into thick, dry curries for eating with Indian bread, whilst **split-hulled lentils** are used for the wet dishes which can be described as soups. They are **ground into flour** for bread, like *Papad, Dosa, Roti*, or made into **thick spongy batter** for fritters and even delicious desserts, e.g. *Besan burfi*, which is a delicious chickpea-flour fudge.

There are many varieties of dried beans and lentils and well-known food products, which because of its large vegetarian population are known to most Indian people.

Adzuki red beans
Tiny reddish brown bean, generally imported from Japan. A few years prior to dying, old men in ancient China, subsisted almost exclusively on them because experience had taught that, when their bodies were exhumed two years after death, they would not emit a foul smell! Popular in Asian cooking and used mainly for sweet dishes in Japan and China.

Barley *jaun*
Sweet tasting, cooling cereal. Diuretic. Dietary fibre found in
barley. Yields significant health benefits, specifically in helping regulate cholesterol levels and hypoglycemia. Decreases
Pitta and Kapha, increases Vata.

Bengal gram *channa dhal*
With skin removed, is a relative of the common chick pea,
called *Channa Dhal*. (Channa dhal is husked, split, whole,
dried, brown chickpeas). Being tasty, nutritious and easy to
digest, channa dhal is roasted and ground into chickpea flour,
besan and is used for savouries, especially in batter, as a bind-
ing agent for fritters, *pakoras* and in sweets.

Black-eyed beans *lobia*
Small, white, kidney-shaped bean with a black spot or 'eye',
called *Lobia*. Used widely in Greek, Middle Eastern and Indian cooking, and very popular in southern USA for soups
and casseroles. Cooked in a green sauce, it is delicious.

Black gram *urid*
Tiny blackish-grey pulse when whole; creamy-coloured when
split and skinned (then known as *urid dhal*). It is the twin
brother of the red adzuki in size and is the milk and honey of
the bean family. Its flavour and texture impart a delightful
sweetness and richness to any soup or vegetable dish. Used in
Indian cooking particularly with rice to make pancakes called
dhosai. When soaked, ground and set aside for a few hours, it
has the property of fermenting and making the mixtures in
which it is used, very light and spongy.

Borlotti, Roman or **Cranberry beans**
Large kidney-shaped bean, always with speckled markings,
they vary in colour considerably from pale pink to dark red or
brown; smooth-textured and happy to absorb other flavours,

these beans are favourites for spicy casseroles, or salads, particularly in Italian cuisine.

Broad, Fava or Faba beans
Large flat bean, olive green through to brown. Often eaten fresh but also used in Mediterranean and Egyptian cooking, where the dried bean is often slow soaked to remove the rather leathery skin before cooking.

Buckwheat *singhara*
Heart friendly. Lowers serum cholesterol and blood pressure.

Butter beans
Very large, plump white bean. Buttery flavoured and floury in texture, butter beans are ideal puree material and go well in salads.

Cannelloni beans
White kidney bean, larger than haricot and squared off at the end. Native to South America, often substituted by Great Northern beans from U.S.A. An Italian favourite for hearty casseroles.

Channa chickpeas
Refers to *Kabuli channa*, Chick peas or garbanzo beans.

Chick peas or garbanzo beans
Hazel-nut shaped, rough textured, coloured cream to fawn, the nutty, earthy flavour is ideal for Middle Eastern dishes such as falafel and hommus. Called *Kabuli channa* in India, they are the bread of the 'pulse-eater.' A main course suggestion is a banquet called *Chole,* savoury chickpeas in a tomato base.

Chickpea flour Gram flour *besan*
Fine-textured flour, creamy yellow in colour, made by dry-

grinding chickpeas. Very versatile medium, used as a base for many sweet dishes, to prepare a batter with which to coat onions and other vegetables before frying to make bhajiyas and as a garnish in final stages of cooking vegetables. Should be stored in a cool dry place.

Chapatti, roti
Unleavened Indian bread, made from fine-textured wholemeal flour. The whole kernel is a good source of dietary fibre, as it contains a high proportion of bran and wheatgerm.

Dhal
An essential part and the protein component of a healthy vegetarian diet. The word 'dhal' means 'dried legumes', which include yellow and green split peas, lentils, mung beans and all other dried beans such as soya, broad, lima, haricot, borlotti, etc. Some people prefer their dhal thin and liquidy, others prefer it so thick that it can be eaten with a fork - the only difference is the amount of water used in relation to the quantity of legume. Try making *Urid dhal Mulligatawny.*

Dhal Chawal lentil rice
An exotic South Indian lentil and rice combination.

Haricot or Navy beans
Small white bean, oval in shape, traditionally used in 'baked beans'. Toss into salads.

Lentil malka, masur
Whole brown or green, small, flattish and round, with a greeny-brown seed coat, called *Malka* in India. They cook quickly without soaking and are frequently used in Indian, Spanish and Middle Eastern cooking as a single vegetable or added to other ingredients.

Red split lentils, called *Masoor dhal* are not consumed by strict followers of the Vedic culture because of their very high protein content.

Lentil bread - wafer thin *pappadams* which incidentaly can also be made in 30 seconds in the microwave, is delicious.

Lima beans
Small green or white, or larger white, these kidney-shaped flat beans resemble butter beans. The sweetish flavour and floury texture makes them suitable for salads or savoury dishes.

Masala Dosa
Urid dhal and rice flour pancakes, a South Indian favourite.

Millet *jovar, bajra*
High in lysine, an essential amino acid, which the body doesn't produce. High in protein, phosphorus, B vitamins and iron. Easy to digest. Cook like rice.

Moghul Rajmah
A rich textured red kidney bean dish.

Mung beans
Tiny moss green or black bean. Can be cooked whole, or split and ground to make Asian sweets. Once the green coat is removed the inside is pale yellow. Also used fresh as sprouts. Called *Moong saboot* in India; split, husked mung is called *Moong dhal*.

Navy
Also known as white **haricot**.

Oats/Oatmeal, Pressed oats
Hulled oat grain that has been rolled or cut into flakes. Oat-

meal is amongst the most nutritious of all the grains, being 16.7% protein, rich in inositol (one of the B-complex vitamins), iron, phosphorous and thiamine. Lowers cholesterol.

Pappadam lentil crispbread
Wafer-thin lentil crispbread, plain or spiced made from dried dhal paste, served as an accompaniment to a full meal, as snacks, or as party nibblers. The brittle disks swell when deep fried or toasted over an open flame. Can also be made in 30 seconds in the microwave.

Peas
Whole or split, green or yellow, called *Mattar ki dhal* in India. Puree as a vegetable or for thick warming pea soup.

Pigeon peas, *toovar*, also called *arhar dhal* or *toor dhal*
Is another of the split lentils well-loved in Indian cooking. They are creamy coloured, paler in colour and flatter than yellow split peas.

Pinto beans
Beige coloured, speckled with brown, similar in shape but smaller than borlotti beans. Staple food of the Mexicans. When cooked, these beans become dusky pink, savoury and smooth-textured.

Quinoa (pronounced 'kin-wah')
'The mother grain.' Very high in protein, calcium, B vitamins and iron. Very easy to digest.

Red gram dhal, *Toor dhal.*
Keeps its shape in cooking.

Red Kidney beans *rajma*
Bright red and yes, kidney shaped. Indispensable in Mexican

re-fried beans, but also smooth enough for soups and salads.

Rice *chawal*
Rice is a staple food. It adds the bulk necessary in the diet and is a source of a number of essential nutrients. A study done at the University of Queensland suggests that nutritionally, polished rice is far superior to white flour.

There are two basic kinds of rice - long grain and short grain - the latter is mainly used for sticky rice dishes.

Brown unpolished rice is considered nutritionally superior. In the polishing and bleaching process, some of its nutrients are removed. For one cup of brown rice, use two cups of water, bring to the boil, then cover and simmer for 35 minutes. Go and meditate. Craters will form as the steam leaves the rice. Turn off and leave for a further five minutes.

Basmati rice superb, light-textured long grain, aromatic rice with wonderful fragrance and flavour is easy to cook and although more costly than other long-grain rice, is well worth the extra expense. Even served plain with a little ghee, or butter, basmati rice is a treat.

Poha, flat, pounded rice is often deep-fried and added to fried potato straws, peanuts and raisins and eaten as a tasty snack.

Jasmine rice is a delicious long-grain, aromatic white rice from Thailand, sometimes called Thai rice. It cooks to large, soft, fluffy grains, and when fed to dogs, helps eliminate that 'doggie' smell from their coats.

Semolina *sooji*
The first millings of the endosperm, when the wheat germ, bran and endosperm are separated in the middle stages of

flour milling hard durum-wheat grains.

Ground fine, medium or coarse, semolina is simmered for
fluffy sweet *halva* puddings or savoury vegetable dishes called
upma.

Soya
Small, oval-shaped bean, very hard and usually buff-coloured.
The most nutritious of beans but they require long cooking
and are uninspiring in flavour. Best combined with other
ingredients or used when converted to bean curd, (Tofu) soy
sauce or paste.

Soybeans are rich in fibre and contain specific phytochemicals
(biologically active substances found only in plants) that are
potent anti-oxidants. Ideal for those who wish to eliminate
animal protein from their diets, eating 25 gms of soya protein a
day has been shown to reduce serum cholesterol, provide
protection against cancer and help in reducing the risk of
several chronic illnesses, including diabetes, osteoporosis, high
blood pressure and kidney disease.

Miso (bean paste) and *shoyu* (soy sauce) are two more soy bean
products that are fundamental to Japanese food. See *tempeh*,
tofu, soya beans.

Split Peas *mattar*
Skinned and split, green or yellow dried peas are especially
good for cooking into a creamy puree.

Tahini Sesame paste
A semi-liquid sesame butter. This creamy-grey paste has the
consistency of runny peanut butter and is delicious instead of
butter, as the base for salad sandwiches and various salad
dressings.

Tempeh

Tempeh maximises the utilisation of the whole soybean and is the soyafood with the highest protein and fibre. It's popularity is because of its chewy, textured, tasty, nutty flavour. Being protein-rich, tempeh is the most 'meat-like' fermented soyfood, comprised of soybeans, rice or grains. High in B2, B3, B6 and B12, it has also been found to contain a natural anti-oxidant that stops the soybean from going rancid and protects the vitamin E content. It is eaten chopped up, steamed or lightly fried and added to stir-fries, stews and soups. In spite of its popularity, I do not endorse fermented products like tempeh or vinegar.

Tic Beans *foulia*

Tofu *Soya paneer*

Soybean curd or tofu is white, almost tasteless and odourless produced from soya beans that have been successively crushed, boiled in water, strained and pressed into a mould. The left-over milk is curdled and set into firm rubbery blocks. As most of the soybean is disposed of in this process, only 8% of the bean's protein is captured in tofu. It is low in calories, low in fibre, salt and fat, cholesterol-free and high in calcium. Silken tofu is lightly pressed with the consistency of firm custard. A firmer variety is also available, which is good for slicing, cubing (eg. in salads) and deep-frying.

It is a mainstay of the Japanese diet. Eat it for breakfast, lunch and/or dinner. Its flavour is so delicate that it might be mistaken for custard that is neither sweet nor savoury. It has been called the food of a thousand flavours — all of which you provide!

Urid - see black gram, this list.

29.5 OILS

Many of the low grade essential oils with chemical extenders are not safe. In addition, oils used for recreational fragrances and flavourings are distilled using high temperatures and powerful chemicals to enhance potency but the therapeutic value is mostly destroyed. It's the difference between eating a fresh strawberry and strawberry flavoured jelly. The real strawberry has all the complex natural constituents of whole food direct from nature's table. The jelly has almost nothing to do with real strawberries. Essential oils have complex properties that work like electrical frequencies to 'remind' cells of what they need to do to function properly. They balance, protect, invigorate, relax, renew and regulate.

Oils consist chemically of both saturated and unsaturated fats. Natural oils and fats play an important role in a balanced diet and are in the realm of therapeutic foods. Vegetable oils are richer in unsaturated or essential fatty acids (EFAs) and for this reason are better for you than heavy fats of animal origin, like butter and lard. Because the fatty acids contained in vegetable oils are unsaturated, they are able to combine with minerals, proteins and oxygen in the body, and in this way encourage normal cell metabolism and oxidation. If your diet is low in EFAs, particular omega-3, these functions are interfered with and over a period of years, cells degenerate which inevitably lead to disease.

Cold pressed oil is best as oils that are heat treated are very hard to digest.

Omega-3 and omega-6 produce the protective membranes which surround each cell. With approximately 20 million cells per square centimetre in the body, a depletion of EFAs can adversely affect nearly every organ and biochemical function.

Cells need the omega-3 and omega-6 fatty acids to adequately strengthen and repair, which in turn assists in the healthy functioning of all our organs.

The easiest way is to have four dessertspoons of a natural oil containing both omega-3 and omega-6 a day, consumed in salads, or as a spread.

Flaxseed oil - linseed - is an excellent source of EFAs (essential fatty acids). Benefits of flaxseed oil include prevention and treatment of arthritis and asthma. Its uniquely high level of omega-3 is helpful in the management and treatment of heart disease and cancer.

After flaxseed, **canola oil** is the next valuable source of omega-3 fatty acids and is particularly beneficial for the cardiovascular system. Both oxidise easily, creating free radicals and are not recommended for cooking.

Olive Oil - The oil extracted from the fruit of the Mediterranean tree, *Olea europaea*, olive oil has a modest quantity of omega-6 fatty acids and no omega-3, but because the composition of fat molecules in olive oil is the closest to those found in mother's milk, it is one of the most acceptable kinds of oil for human consumption and assimilation.

The finest olive oil is raw, cold pressed from fresh, ripe olives, has a greenish colour and is rich in chlorophyll. Extra virgin olive oil contains polyphenols and aqualane which are powerful anti-oxidants and is best eaten unheated to get the most from its nutrients. More crude versions of olive oil are second pressings, made under heat, with a high smoking point for cooking.

Choosing olive oil is a matter of personal taste and preference.

Suggest have two grades of oil in the kitchen: mild cold pressed
extra-virgin olive oil for salads and uncooked dishes and a pure grade
olive oil.

Peanut oil, also known as **ground-nut oil** *moong phali tel*
High quality, more expensive peanut oil comes from cold
pressing. Lesser-quality peanut oils are produced with the aid
of chemical solvents. The oil is then refined and heated and
treated with anti-oxidants. Used for deep frying, usually
because peanut oil has a smoking point of up to 230C/450F
and has a bland flavour.

Safflower oil *kusumbha*
Low in saturated fatty acids, has a mild flavour, a high smoking point and is suitable as a salad oil or a deep-frying oil.

Sesame seeds and oil, *til*
The flat pear-shaped seeds are generally lightly roasted to
bring out their nutty flavour. High in calcium, rich in thiamine, they are very popular ground into a semi-liquid paste
called *tahini*. The seeds are a diuretic and therefore prescribed
for urinary disorders. They are also used for dysmenorrhoea,
especially in the cases of irregular menstruation in pubescent
girls. Reduces susceptibility to oxidative stress.

I know of two types of sesame oil. One is expressed from the
roasted seeds of the annual plant and is much favoured as a
flavouring agent in Chinese and Korean cooking. This delicate
brown oil has a low smoking-point and a delicious roasted-
sesame flavour and is generally added as a final seasoning to a
cooked dish.

The golden oil expressed from the oil-rich unroasted sesame
seeds has a slightly sweet smell and a clean taste. It has a
higher smoking-point than roasted sesame oil and is used both

as a salad oil and is especially popular as a frying oil, because it does not turn rancid, even in the hottest weather. Like olive oil, it is now considered an oil that lowers high cholesterol.

Due to its rejuvenating effect and particular effectiveness in reducing stress and fatigue, the oil is used for daily massage.

29.6 DAIRY

Cheese
Yellow cheese gets the thumbs down for its melt and stretch qualities in the colon, as it does on a pizza. Home-made cheese, called **Paneer**, however, is a different matter.

Dahi yoghurt
See Yoghurt.

Dahi Wada
Lentil cakes in Yoghurt.

Ghee clarified butter
Ghee adds a distinctive flavour to food. It is the oil produced by clarifying butter over a gentle heat until all the moisture is evaporated and the milk-solid fats are fully separated from the clear butter fat. It can be bought in tins, or sometimes cartons. Can be heated to a much higher temperature than ordinary butter without burning because the impurities from the butter have been removed (which is what burns when butter is heated).

Milk

Yoghurt *Dahi*
Healthful cultured dairy product, the easiest way to digest dairy milk and an accessible source of calcium, B vitamins and vitamin E.

When the 'friendly' bacteria found in milk are left to turn it sour, this natural action allows milk to form into other culture-rife dairy products, like yoghurt, curds and whey. Lactobacillus acidophilus are the naturally occurring bacteria involved in this fermentation process, which holistic medical literature is full of information about linking it to improved digestive functions. Acidophilus is one of the beneficial lactobacillus bacteria normally found in the digestive tract. A regular intake of yoghurt or any fermented milk product is a good way of maintaining a healthy bowel ecology and protecting it from potentially damaging toxins. Yoghurt is versatile with a pleasant tangy flavour and smooth, refreshing texture, useful for relieving digestive problems such as irregular bowel movements, bloating and intestinal discomfort.

In Indian cuisine, yoghurt is eaten as an accompaniment to savoury dishes and not with fruit and sugar as eaten in the West. The most suitable yoghurt is one which is thick set and made from whole milk. Other types of natural yoghurt have a high water content and will make gravy watery and do little to enhance the flavour of dishes.

Eating yoghurt for Pitta, and for all doshas in the evening is contraindicated in Ayurveda.

29.7 WATER

Water performs many functions of the body, it regulates temperature, takes part in all chemical processes and digestion of food, lubricates many parts and protects the body from injury. It is the principal fluid in blood and furnishes a medium for absorption, metabolism, secretion and excretion. Insufficient water intake causes incomplete elimination, with resulting body wastes accumulating to escape some other way, other than by natural means. Hydration is an area of health often overlooked.

Water is lost through sweat, urination and breathing. Each day you lose about 18 glasses of water through all the eliminative processes of your body. About 11 glasses of this comes from food and the rest from liquid intake. When you feel thirst your body is sending a message that it requires water , not soft drink, juice, beer, or coffee. Drinking ten glasses of water a day will reduce feelings of tiredness and grogginess.

Tap water is a refreshing, inexpensive, zero-energy (zero calories/kilojoules) way to replace lost fluid. Drinking large quantities of water helps reduce the formation of uric acid crystals which cause the pain and discomfort of gout and other ailments.

There is no new water. The water we drink today has been on this planet since the beginning of time. Unfortunately we pollute this most precious liquid with insecticides, pesticides, factory wastes and other contaminants which find their way into rivers, lakes and dams. Reservoirs are treated with chlorine and other chemicals to cleanse it for human use. These chemicals contribute to the bad taste and odour that many people experience and dislike. With the chemicals in tap water, many people opt for natural and mineral water, which tastes soft and fresh even at room temperature. If you are watching your sodium intake, check the kilojoule, chemical and salt content of the packaged products.

FIRST STEPS IN AYURVEDIC VEGETARIAN COOKING

Creative sauce-making uses the gifts of natural oils, seeds, herbs and spices for delicious taste as well as for cleansing and healing. Be light and subtle. The recipes are to help you get started. Before you know it, you will invent your own blends. In time, you will just use your nose and senses, leaving your mind and memory behind.

30. THE HAPPY COOK
The kitchen is the heart of the home.

A happy person in the kitchen fills everyone in the house with joy. Cutting vegetables, kneading flour, singing a song - these gestures are as beautiful as the waltzing of flowers in the field. Food prepared by a calm and happy cook in a pleasant environment has the best influence.

Wash your hands and the produce before you start preparing the meal. Take a slow, deep breath, centre yourself by chanting Om ... and then begin.

Food should always be fresh, of the best quality and preferably organic and whole foods. Place great emphasis on freshness, quality and foods in season. Traditionally Ayurvedic cooks shop every day so they are certain of the freshness of the ingredients. Complex systems of nutrition based on colours, shapes and ratios found in whole foods have a remarkable ability to carry healing and nourishing 'information' to the cells of your body.

Let your meal stand apart from the usual fare of fast and convenience food because of its simplicity and purity. Memorable, not for their over-spicing, richness or complex blending of flavours, but because of the vibes, emphasis on basic ingredients and the development of a palate that accepts and appreciates food in its most natural, pleasurable and nourishing state. It is preferable to avoid left-over or reheated food where possible.

Place the lentils and beans to cook first as they take longer. Chop and prepare all the vegetables and have your ingredients ready before you commence cooking their sauce. Food is best when warm and well cooked. Overcooked, undercooked or burnt food is not good.

Cook in a peaceful way. Try not to make false or violent movements with the spoon when stirring the pot. Turning it one way, keep the pace and your patience, ease the direction of the spiral, then change it if necessary.

The produce and milk once given to the calf takes new forms. It is now in the pots and pans which are handled by you with love and care. Utensils are part of the body. Choose their volume and shape appropriately. Either there is poetry in the dish, for this flavour and food comes from God to us, ennobling our everyday acts, or there is no poetry at all, just murder, cooked with a sad face and a bitter heart.

Politics and wars are also symbols of the hunger of people who have been ill-fed ... struggling all their lives towards a giant feast of conquest and power, never satisfied by a simple bowl of rice and vegetables. Their parents were bad cooks and now they suffer similar circumstances with their spouses, themselves and fast food producers. It is urgent that new recipes founded in love and peace be written.

The cook should know that s/he is the centre of the ecological problem! Ecology starts in the belly, not outside us … ecology starts in the belly, because our environment is a reflection of ourselves. A beautiful vegetable is not necessarily as straight as a soldier on parade. It is disconcerting to see priced and packaged carrots of the same form and size lined up like legionnaires in supermarkets. It amounts to biological communism, to a brutal indoctrination of the vegetable world. In the modern world we must be alert to the changes wrought on carrots and cauliflowers, pumpkins and peas by the chemical industry and the farmer it has so easily duped. If our tastes are simple, our environment will be clean; but if our tastes are physiologically and psychologically distorted by the current advertising, then the lakes will be full of mercury and other ingredients of ill health. Human beings can still provide for the serenity and beauty of the world if they know of a clean diet - and in Ayurveda, it is one that that leaves no waste.

While for some of the meal you will use oil and/or ghee as a cooking medium, for other parts of the meal you will cook in or over water. Water-based cooking gives a lightness and delicacy of flavour that is most appealing. Steaming means that the pure flavours of the food and most of the food value are retained. As a result, you have a balanced meal that will keep you and your family strong, healthy and with disease at bay.

Food should always look, smell and taste delicious. Think - beautiful presentation. Serve smaller quantities, more variety, appreciate appearance, aroma, taste, texture and that certain attitude towards food - considered not only good for the body but also for the soul. Pay some attention to the bowl or plate on which you present the food. Summer foods, cool and light can be set off by green leaves and delicate plates, while winter brings on steaming food to be eaten at the table. Cultivate the surroundings in which the meal is eaten carefully so that a peaceful atmosphere prevails.

31. PRAYER BEFORE THE MEAL

Whatever you eat is Mother Nature in the form of food. The fruits are your mother, the grains are your mother, the whole earth is your mother. Food is from Nature. Air is from Nature. Water is from Nature. We take things from Nature, so let us return things to her. We cannot return exactly what we take but we can convert the food, air and water into energy and utilise that energy for the benefit of the world. Then we are not debtors.

Affirmation

We give blessings and thanks to Mother Nature
and all her gifts that come to our table as food.

Earth, water, fire, air and space, present in nature
and also within us as health, strength, wisdom and dispassion.

We bless and give thanks to the cook
and all the producers of this meal.

We eat with great joy and celebration with all who are eating with us
and have a special heart for those who are hungry.

Mother Nature is the form of food,
let me reciprocate your love,
let this food be converted into wisdom and dispassion,
so that I am a better person and a useful person.

Make this meal and all meals a blessing to all.
I thank God for granting me the freedom
to eat whatever I need to stay healthy.

Hari Om Tat Sat : Beloved, you are that Truth.

In addition to the joy and celebration we can add this to our purpose in eating. In conclusion, if you obsess about the food you eat, let me add that **it's not so much what you eat, but what's eating you**...

32. MEASUREMENTS OF INGREDIENTS

cup	Metric 250 ml
dts	dessert spoon
lge	large
med	medium
ml	millilitre
grd	ground
sml cubes	1cm squares (approx.)
tbs	table spoon
tsp	tea spoon
to taste	quantity as per personal taste

33. UTENSILS

• A **brush** to scrub dirt and mud off the vegetables under cold running water. (I rarely soak or peel vegetables).

• A **colander** is a must in every kitchen. It comes in handy for rinsing noodles and washing fruits, such as cherries, straw berries and grapes.

• A metal or porcelain **grater** is indispensable for grating lemon-rind, ginger, etc.

• **Knives**. Choose the best quality knives you can afford.

• **A wooden cutting board**, or plastic. One that doesn't blunt the knives as much.

• **Stainless steel pots & pans** are best. Use the heaviest pots you can find, be they enamelled, cast-iron, stainless steel, glassware or earthenware. The thicker they are, the less acid your food will be. Aluminium pots, in addition to the fact that they produce poison when the food is allowed to stand in them for any reasonable length of time, do not provide the fine taste that results from the use of earthenware or heavy enamelled cast-iron pots.

• A stainless steel **pressure cooker** retains all the nutritious elements which would normally evaporate in a normal pot, except for those with very heavy lids, which are difficult to find.

• A stainless steel **steamer**, or a Japanese bamboo steamer has many uses, from heating rice to preparing couscous.

• A tawa, or **Frying Pan** - for pancakes, chappatis.
• A **deep-fryer** for samosas and pappadams.

34. OIL/GHEE

• A variety of oils, which include: Olive oil; Sunflower oil; Corn oil; Black sesame oil.
• Ghee is clarified butter, available in the dairy section of the supermarket.
Generally 1 tablespoon of oil for 250g of vegetables.

35. HERBS & SPICES

Herbs can be used in the forms of **SEEDS,** generally at the early preparation stage of the sauce.
eg. mustard seeds, cummin seeds, fenugreek, cardamom pods, sesame seeds, poppy seeds.

Herbs can be used after being dried and **GROUND**
eg. cummin ground; coriander ground; chili, pepper, cloves, cinnamon.

Herbs can be used **FRESH**
- generally added just before serving, eg. coriander, dill, parsley, mint.

Mix your favourite combinations. For example:

Italian Seasonings:
Oregano + Basil + Rosemary + Thyme + Paprika

Salad Herbs:
Chives + Parsley + Basil + Tarragon + Mint + Garlic

Garam Masala
Keep in airtight container for ready use as seasoning.

36. THE BASIC SAUCE INGREDIENTS

The sauces for basic Ayurvedic cooking include the use of:

Fresh onion
Fresh ginger
Fresh garlic
Fresh coriander leaves
Fresh lemon grass
Fresh parsley
Fresh mint
Fresh tomatoes
Black mustard seeds
Cummin seeds
Ground Tumeric
Chilli powder

Tamarind	added to a dish gives a salty flavour.
Asafoetida	a pinch added to onions in the *Basic sauce* will prevent wind (flatulence) that could occur from eating *Pulses*.
Ginger:	Wash ginger root & grate on coarse side of grater. Add to onions in *Basic sauce*.
Garlic:	Peel garlic & crush or cut into small pieces. Can then be added to onions in *Basic sauce*.

Fresh ginger root and garlic cloves give a special dash & addition to a dish. Add to taste.

All the following recipes have been kitchen tested.

36.1 HOW TO MAKE THE BASIC SAUCE

Oil	1 dts Olive/Sunflower
Mustard seeds	$1/_2$ tsp
Cummin seeds	$1/_2$ tsp
Curry leaves	4-5 crushed
Onion	1 medium
Ginger	to taste
Garlic	to taste
Turmeric grd	$1/_4$ tsp
Chilli grd	pinch
Asafoetida	pinch (to prevent flatulence)

In a small quantity of hot oil, in a heavy, deep saucepan (test the heat of the oil) add approx. $1/_2$ tsp **brown mustard seeds**. When the seeds pop, like popcorn, immediately add an equal quantity of **cummin seeds**. As their aroma and goodness are released, which will be fairly immediate, no time to meditate here, add 4-5 **crushed curry leaves** and **chopped onion** and saute until transparent in the hot seed-oil. Add **ginger** and/or **garlic** for more zest. A pot-pourri of spices and herbs can be added next. $1/_4$ tsp of **ground turmeric**, a pinch of **chilli powder**, a pinch of **asafoetida** are rarely excluded. Stir together. Your Basic Sauce is ready. Use as a base for cooking.

NOTE:
If you use a shallow frying pan (don't) you will need a lid or the hot seeds will fly out of the pot onto every surface of your kitchen and possibly onto you!

To **test oil temperature**, drop 3 mustard seeds into the oil, & repeat this until they move around & pop immediately, the temperature is then correct; this is when you add the measured seeds. Popping the seeds releases their healing properties. If the oil is too hot and the seeds burn, discard the entire batch and start again. If the oil is too cool, the seeds will absorb the oil and will not pop.

37. VEGETABLES

37.1 VEGETABLES - PREPARATION

Wash vegetables to remove dust etc. Peel if required. However, leave the skin on most vegetables including potatoes, for better nutrition that is just underneath the skin and for added fibre.

Cut into small cubes/pieces. Smaller pieces lessen the cooking time and food that is cooked quickly, holds its nutritional value.

37.2 VEGETABLES - COOKING

Vegetables have varying firmness and texture. When cooking two or more vegetables together, be aware that some may need more cooking than others and allow for this.

37.3 TIME SAVING HINTS

When in a hurry to put dinner on the table, the steaming of potato, pumpkin, swede, turnip etc. will speed up the process, then add to *Basic sauce*. (Nutrition is not lost when steamed.) Retain the water for your cooking as it contains many water-soluble vitamins.

37.4 VEGETABLE COMBINATIONS TO TRY

Cabbage & tomato
Carrots & beans
Cauliflower & broccoli
Celery & sweet corn
Potato & cauliflower
Potato & pumpkin
Potato, swede & turnip
Spinach & tofu
Spinach & tomato
Zucchini & squash

Note: Allow for variation in texture when cooking vegetables, eg. (Hard & soft)

Cabbage

Ingredients:

Basic sauce   see page N⁰ 137
Cabbage   1 cup per person, chopped finely
Coconut   1 tblsp per person, dessicated
Sultanas   1 tblsp per person
Cashews   to taste, raw

Begin with **Basic sauce.**
Add **cabbage, coconut, sultanas, nuts,** mixing all ingredients together.
Cook until cabbage is transparent and reduced to half its original volume.
Stir well, adding salt to taste.
Take off heat and serve.

Potato - *Aloo*

Ingredients:

Basic sauce   see page N⁰ 137
Potato   1 med. per person, steamed, sml cubes
               Scrub, do not peel
Coriander   1 bunch, chopped finely

Begin with **Basic sauce.**
Add **potato** mixing all ingredients together, adding salt to taste.
Stir in **Coriander** just before serving.
Take off heat and serve.

Potato & Cauliflower - *Aloo-Gobi*

Ingredients:
Basic sauce   see page Nº 137
Potato   1 small per person, steamed, small cubes
Cauliflower $^3/_4$ cup per person, raw, small flowerettes.
Garam Masala   to taste

Begin with **Basic sauce.**
Add **potato & cauliflower** mixing all ingredients together.
Stir in Garam Masala, adding salt to taste.
Cover, lower heat, allow potato & cauliflower to cook until firm, not soggy.
Take off heat and serve.

Spinach & Potato – Saag Aloo

Ingredients:
Basic sauce   see page Nº 137
Potato   1 med. per person, steamed, sml cubes
Spinach   1 lge cup per person, fresh
Ginger   to taste, coarsely grated, fresh
Garlic   to taste, finely chopped, fresh
Chilli grd   to taste

Begin with **Basic sauce.**
Adding **garlic** and **ginger** to onions, stir in chilli & add **potatoes** mixing all ingredients together, adding salt to taste.
Place **spinach** on top, cover, lower heat and allow spinach to wilt.
Take off heat, mix, serve.

Spinach - *Saag*

Ingredients:

Spinach/Silverbeet	2 cups raw per person
Ginger	to taste, grated coarsely, fresh
Tomato	sml cubes - optional
Tofu	sml cubes - optional
Ghee	1 lge dsts

Heat ghee in saucepan.
Add ginger, cook lightly.
Add spinach/silverbeet & salt, turn down heat & let cook
down until soft.
Remove from heat & vitamize until smooth.
Stir in tomato &/or tofu & serve.

Zucchini

Ingredients:

Basic sauce	see page N$^{o.}$ 137
Zucchini	1 cup per person, sml cubes
Sweet corn	$^{1}/_{2}$ cob per person, kernels removed from cob
Tomato	small cubes - optional

Begin with **Basic sauce**.
Add **sweet corn kernels**, partially cook.
Add **zucchini** & cook further.
Add salt to taste, stir in **tomato** just before serving.
Take off heat and serve.

Pumpkin

Ingredients:

Basic sauce	see page Nº· 137
Tomatoes	$^1/_2$ per person, sml cubes
Pumpkin	1 cup per person, sml cubes
Garlic	to taste, chopped finely, fresh
Chilli grd	to taste
Coconut	$^1/_2$ cup, dessicated
Shallots-green	raw, chopped.
Chick peas	500 gms pre-cooked (optional)

Begin with **Basic sauce**.
Add **tomatoes,** letting them soften into the sauce.
Then add **pumpkin, garlic & ginger** mixing ingredients together.
Place lid on saucepan, lower heat & allow to cook until soft.
Add a little water if it becomes too dry.
When cooked add coconut and shallots, adding salt to taste.
Note : To make this into a more substantial dish, add chick-peas. If using butternut pumpkin, there is no need to peel.

Broccoli

Ingredients:

Basic sauce	see page Nº· 137
Broccoli	$^3/_4$ cup per person - raw, coarsely grated
Coconut	1 tblsp per person, dessicated

Begin with **Basic sauce**, add **broccoli & coconut** mixing all ingredients together, adding salt to taste.
Take off heat and serve.
Note: Broccoli should be served almost raw.

Earthen Combo

Ingredients:

Basic sauce	see page N$^{o.}$ 137
Potato	sml cubes - $^1/_2$ cup per person, steamed
Swede	sml cubes - $^1/_4$ cup per person, steamed
Turnip	sml cubes - $^1/_4$ cup per person, steamed
Garam Masala	to taste

Begin with **Basic sauce**.

Stir-in Garam Masala.

Add **potatoes, swede & turnip**, mixing all ingredients together & salt to taste.

Take off heat and serve.

PULSES, LENTILS, BEANS & GRAINS

PREPARATION

To do this fill a large bowl with water and swish around measured pulses to remove any dust etc. Tip bowl slightly to empty out water and repeat process until water is clear.

Fill bowl with water again, letting pulses soak for a few hours or overnight.

Note: Large pulses such as chick-peas are better when soaked overnight. **Quick method** : Bring pulses to the boil, tip the first water off and then start the cooking process.

METHOD

Pulses are best cooked in a stainless-steel pressure cooker - quicker and digested easier.

Using **Basic sauce** add **Pulses** - any beans, lentils etc., **water,** salt, **spices** to taste. Cook until soft.

Important: add Asofetida to onions when cooking *Basic sauce* for the prevention of flatulence which could occur if pulses are poorly digested.

Chick-Peas - *Channa*

Basic sauce	see page N⁰· 137
Chick-peas	250 gms soaked overnight
Bay-leaves	6
Cinnamon quills	2
Cloves	6
Cardamom pods	6
Water	700 mls
Salt	1 tsp.

Start with Basic sauce.
Combine all ingredients in pressure cooker and stir.
Cook for approx 15-20 minutes once pressure has been
reached. Check. If too hard, cook longer.

Chick-Pea Dip - Hommus

Ingredients:

Chick-peas	2 cups soaked overnight & cook (see p.146)
Garlic (fresh)	3 cloves, crushed
Tahini	4 tbls
Lemon juice	to taste - lime is better, if available
Cummin ground	1 pinch
Paprika ground	1 pinch
Cayenne pepper	1 pinch
Oil	10 ml - Olive /Sunflower
Vegie salt	to taste

Place cooked chick-peas and peeled garlic cloves in electric blender / food processsor and blend until it is a thick, smooth consistency.

Add tahini, lemon juice, spices and vegie salt to taste. Continue blending until the mix becomes a smooth, creamy paste. If it is too thick, add water to dilute and continue to mix.

Can be kept in an airtight container for 2 weeks in the refrigerator.

Serve as a dip with carrot & celery sticks, as a spread on bread or biscuits or accompanying meals.

Tofu - preparation & cooking method

($^1/_3$ cup per person - small cubes)

Tofu can be added to cooking direct from packaging or
marinated in Soy sauce or your choice of marinade.

Add Tofu to dish (from packaging) just before serving, or
lightly fry & then add to dish.

Peas and Tofu

Basic sauce	see page N° 137
Tofu	1 packet, firm, cubed
Peas	100 gms, shelled
Tomatoes	to taste
Ginger	to taste
Coriander	to taste
Vegetable stock	to desired consistency
Salt	to taste

Into the basic sauce, add peas, tomatoes, ginger, tofu and
saute.
Add vegetable stock and stir.
Cook in pressure cooker. approx 15 mins.
Add chopped coriander and serve.

Scrambled Tofu

Corn oil	2 tsp, cold pressed
Spring onions	4, chopped
Tumeric	$1/_2$ tsp
Tofu	250 gms, mashed
Shoyu, salt-free	2 tsp
Vegie seasoning	$1/_2$ tsp, salt-free
Parsley	2 tbs fresh, chopped

Heat oil in non-stick frypan with onion & tumeric.
Saute 2 mins.
Add remaining ingredients and stir for 5-6 mins.
Season with freshly ground black pepper and parsley.
Use on wholemeal toast with grilled tomatoes, or as a salad filling.

Tofu loaf

Tofu	500 gms, mashed
Onion	1 large, finely chopped
Celery	1 stick, finely chopped
Garlic	2 cloves, crushed
Breadcrumbs	1 cup
Oats-rolled	1 cup
Tahini	2 tbs
Tamari	2 tbs, salt-free
Garam masala	2 tsp
Tomato paste	$^1/_2$ cup natural salt & preservative free
Parsley	$^1/_2$ cup freshly chopped
Tomato paste	$^1/_3$ cup extra

Combine all ingredients thoroughly (except last 2) and press into a lightly oiled baking dish.
Combine parsley and extra tomato paste, spread over the top of the loaf, then sprinkle with sesame seeds.
Bake 1 hour in a medium oven.
Stand 10 mins before cutting.

Serve hot with steamed vegetables, or cold with salad.
Use as a filling for sandwiches, jaffles, pies, pastries, rolls.

RICE - PREPARATION & METHOD

Rice White/Brown $^1/_2$ cup per person - raw
Water ratio   Jasmine, Calrose (short grain) - 1 : 1 water
                          Basmati (long grain) - 1 rice :$1^1/_2$ water
                          Brown - 1 cup rice to 2 cups water
Cooking Time   White rice 10-15 min.
                          Brown rice 30-35 min.

Basmati is the best rice. Long grain separates, whereas short fat grains, like Calrose are used for rice puddings etc.

Wash rice thoroughly, stirring with hand, to rinse away any starch (makes rice less sticky and less fattening). White rice may need rinsing 8-10 times until water has changed from cloudy to transparent. Be careful not to break the rice grains whilst rinsing.

Rice - steamed

Place measured/washed rice in steamer adding water to the depth of the first knuckle on your index finger. Cover, press button to cook. Approx. 30 mins.

Rice - absorbtion method

Place measured/washed rice in saucepan, eg. 1 cup washed rice to 2 cups water.
Bring to the boil, cover, turn temperature down to simmer, allowing rice to absorb the water.
When little craters appear in rice (steam escaping or rice will be soggy) it is cooked. So avoid stirring the rice whilst cooking.
Turn off & leave for 5 minutes.
If rice grain is white and hard in the centre, it needs to cook longer.

Fragrant Rice

Rice	$^1/_2$ cup per person - raw
Bay leaves	2
Cloves	4
Green cardamom pods	6
Cinnamom stick	$^1/_2$
Saffron threads	2-3 sml
Ghee	2 tbls

Wash rice, see page 152
Add water and all other ingredients in saucepan and cook as
per instructions.
When cooked, add ghee.

Yoghurt Smoothie - *Lassi*

Yoghurt (natural)	1 cup
Mango, fresh is best	1 medium
or Banana, fresh	1 medium
or your choice of fresh fruit	1 cup
Rose water	5 ml
Water (fresh)	1 cup
Honey	to taste - optional
Approximate measurements	make to taste

Vitamize all ingredients in a jug until smooth.
Use honey as the sweetner (optional) ...
or Black salt for a more tart taste.
Pour into a glass & serve.

INDEX: NATURAL KITCHEN PHARMACY

BIBLIOGRAPHY

Abehsera Michel, **Cooking for Life**, Avon Books, U.S.A.,1972

Acciardo, Marcia Madhuri, **Light Eating for Survival**, 21st Century Publications, Fairfield, Ia.

Baljekar, Mridula, **Complete Indian Cookbook**, Colour Library Books, 1992

Berg, Alan, **The Nutrition Factor**, The Brookings Institution, Washington D.C., 1973

Bisen Malini, **Vegetable Delights**, Wilco Publishing House, Bombay, 1976

CSIRO Division of **Human Nutrition** Report, 1975-76, Commonwealth Scientific and Industrial Research Organisation, Australia, 1977.

Dasa, Kurma, **Great Vegetarian Dishes**, The Bhaktivedanta Book Trust, NSW Australia. 1990.

Dey, Kanny Lall, et. al, **The Indigenous Drugs of India**, Thacker, Spink & Co. 1984

Editorial Committee, Science of Life Books, **Eating for Health**, Science of Life Books, Melbourne, 1971

Editorial Committee, Science of Life Books, **Live Longer & Healthier,** Science of Life Books, Melbourne, 1972

Frawley, David, and Lad, Vasant, **The Yoga of Herbs**, Lotus Press, Twin Lakes, WI, 1986

Garde, Dr. R.K., **Ayurveda for Health and Long Life**, D.B. Taraporevale Sons & Co., India, 1975

Gowans, Shanti, **Health & Wellbeing,** Inner Peace Publications, Australia, 2001

Indian Vegetarian Congress, **The Vegetarian Way**, World Vegetarian Congress, 1977

Jaffrey Kenneth S., **Living Naturally,** Townsville, Australia 1974

Jaffrey Kenneth S., **Natural Foods**, Townsville, Australia 1974

Johari, Harish, **The Healing Cuisine**, Healing Arts Press,1994

Kloss, Jethro, **Back to Eden**, Lancer Books Inc., New York, 1971

Kulkarni, Prof. Dr. P.H., **Ayurveda Aahar**, Ayurveda Education Series, Pune, India. 1998

Langley, Gill, **Vegan Nutrition - A Survey of Research**, The Vegan Society Ltd., Oxford, 1988

Lovelock, Yann, **The Vegetable Book**, George Allen & Unwin Ltd. 1972

Mehta. K.R., **Vegetarian Delights**, Wilshire Book Company, California, 1973.

Phillips, David A., **Guide Book to Nutritional Factors in Edible Foods**, Pythagorean Press, Sydney, 1977

Powell, Eric F.W., **Health from the Kitchen**, Health Science Press, Rustington, Sussex, 1969

Rau, Santha Rama, and the Editors of Time-Life Books, **The Cooking of India**, Time-Life Books, 1978

Shears, Curtis C., **Nutritional Science & Health Education**, Castle Press, Berkeley, Gloucestershire, 1974

Wilson, D. Geoffrey, **Food is Energy: How to use it**, Boolarong Publications, Brisbane, 1988